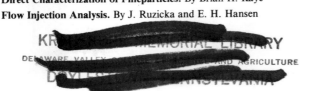

Applied Electron Spectroscopy
For Chemical Analysis

CHEMICAL ANALYSIS

A SERIES OF MONOGRAPHS ON
ANALYTICAL CHEMISTRY AND ITS APPLICATIONS

VOLUME 63

A WILEY-INTERSCIENCE PUBLICATION

JOHN WILEY & SONS

New York / Chichester / Brisbane / Toronto / Singapore

Applied Electron Spectroscopy For Chemical Analysis

HASSAN WINDAWI

UOP Corporate Research Center
UOP Inc.
Des Plaines, Illinois

FLOYD F.-L. HO

Hercules Research Center
Hercules Incorporated
Wilmington, Delaware

A WILEY-INTERSCIENCE PUBLICATION

JOHN WILEY & SONS
New York / Chichester / Brisbane / Toronto / Singapore

Library of Congress Cataloging in Publication Data
Main entry under title:

Applied electron spectroscopy for chemical analysis.

(Chemical analysis; v. 63)
"A Wiley-Interscience publication."
Includes index.
1. Electron spectroscopy. I. Windawi, Hassan,
1942- . II. Ho, Floyd. III. Series.
QD96.E44A66   543'.085   82-4781
ISBN 0-471-09051-4   AACR2
Printed in the United States of America
10 9 8 7 6 5 4 3 2 1

CONTRIBUTORS

Dennis S. Everhart
Kenan Laboratories of Chemistry
University of North Carolina
Chapel Hill, North Carolina

David M. Hercules
Department of Chemistry
University of Pittsburgh
Pittsburgh, Pennsylvania

Floyd F.-L. Ho
Hercules Research Center
Hercules Incorporated
Wilmington, Delaware

L. L. Kazmerski
Photovoltaics Research Branch
Solar Energy Research Institute
Golden, Colorado

Joseph C. Klein
Department of Chemistry
University of Pittsburgh
Pittsburgh, Pennsylvania

G. E. McGuire
Tektronix Incorporated
P.O. Box 500
Beaverton, Oregon

N. S. McIntyre
Brookhaven National Laboratory
Department of Nuclear Energy
Bldg. 830
Upton, New York

C. J. Powell
Surface Science Division
National Bureau of Standards
Washington, D.C.

Charles N. Reilley
Kenan Laboratories of Chemistry
University of North Carolina
Chapel Hill, North Carolina

J. H. Thomas, III
RCA Laboratories
Princeton, New Jersey

C. D. Wagner
Surfex Company
29 Starview Drive
Oakland, California

H. Windawi
UOP Corporate Research Center
UOP Inc.
Des Plaines, Illinois

PREFACE

Surface phenomena, a very common and yet extremely complex subject, are with us in our daily life as well as in our scientific endeavors, such as investigations in adhesion, catalysis, corrosion, enzymatic reactions, and of various solid state surfaces and interfaces. These studies have benefited greatly from the recent development of various surface-sensitive techniques and instruments. Among these developments is electron spectroscopy for chemical analysis (ESCA), which is also commonly termed x-ray photoelectron spectroscopy (XPS). In addition to its surface sensitivity, ESCA is uniquely capable of providing chemical information such as oxidation state and chemical bonding, as well as elemental compositions. In conjunction with ion milling or chemical etching, it has the ability to furnish a depth profile of both a surface and subsurface. In the last few years, ESCA has rapidly become a useful tool for every scientist dealing with surface properties of various materials. In this regard, a symposium on the chemical application of ESCA was held at the seventh Federation of Analytical Chemistry and Spectroscopy Societies (FACSS) meeting in Philadelphia on October 2, 1980. This monograph is a direct result of this symposium, with most presentations revised and extended to cover pertinent references up to early 1981.

In addition to critical review of major developments, new and significant advances from the authors' own laboratories were described at the symposium. To put the technique of ESCA in proper perspective, the experimental method in ESCA was featured (G. E. McGuire) and compared with other surface-analysis techniques (C. J. Powell). The applications dealing with various surfaces and interfaces of metals and metal oxides, such as solid state devices (J. H. Thomas, III), photovoltaic cells (L. L. Kazmerski), and corrosion processes (N. S. McIntyre) were discussed. Measurement of functional groups on polymer films was highlighted (C. N. Reilley, D. S. Everhart, and F. F.-L. Ho), and development in characterization of polymer-anchored homogeneous catalysts was covered (F. F.-L. Ho). Special features of application in heterogeneous catalysis (D. M. Hercules and J. C. Klein), as well as techniques in dealing with heterogeneous materials in general (H. Windawi and C. D. Wagner), were presented.

It is the editors' particular pleasure to acknowledge herein the contributions and genuine efforts of the individual authors as well as those of the reviewers. The comments and patience of the Series Editors and the publication staff are highly appreciated. We are, nevertheless, grieved by the untimely death of

Professor Charles N. Reilley of the University of North Carolina on December 31, 1981. On a happier note we express our congratulations to K. Siegbahn for being awarded the Nobel prize for 1981, which was partly based on his pioneering work in ESCA.

Hassan Windawi

Des Plaines, Illinois

Wilmington, Delaware   Floyd F.-L. Ho
August 1982

CONTENTS

CHAPTER

1

INSTRUMENTAL METHODS IN ESCA

G. E. McGUIRE

Tektronix Incorporated
Beaverton, Oregon

1. INTRODUCTION

Photoelectron spectroscopy is growing in popularity as a general analytical tool, specifically in the area of surface analysis. In essence, it involves the energy analysis of electrons ejected from matter by incident radiation. It allows the investigation of electronic structure, providing a picture of molecular orbitals for gas-phase species, valence band density of states, and core-level electron-binding energies for solids. The characteristic electron energies allow elemental analysis as well as chemical state identification. In addition, photoelectron spectroscopy probes only the surface region of solids. As a result, the technique is frequently used in investigations of phenomena such as absorption, corrosion, catalysis, adhesion, and segregation, where surface composition is of great importance.

The phenomenon of photoemission when a material is exposed to electromagnetic radiation of sufficient energy has been known for quite a long time. It was not until the late 1960s that significant developments in the field of photoelectron spectroscopy occurred that led to the current awareness of the technique. K. Siegbahn and others in the Physics Department of the University of Uppsala, Sweden, published pioneering works in the field in 1967[1] and 1969[2] which described in detail many aspects of electron spectroscopy as they are known today. In their 1967 study, Siegbahn et al. coined the term *electron spectroscopy for chemical analysis* (ESCA), which is now frequently used interchangeably with *x-ray excited photoelectron spectroscopy* (XPS). About the same time, D. W. Turner and his colleagues at the University of Oxford, England, published their work on *ultraviolet photoelectron spectroscopy* (UPS) of molecular gases.[3] Commercial instrumentation for XPS of solids and UPS of gases became available around 1970. Rapid development of the technique took place over the next few years resulting in a merging of the instrumentation for XPS and UPS. In 1972 a journal was founded that was devoted to the topic, namely, *Journal of Electron Spectroscopy and Related Phenomena.* Nowadays, it is difficult to find a chemical journal that does not contain some articles related to photoelectron spectroscopy. Interest in the application of this technique to surface analysis in a wide variety of fields has resulted in several international conferences[4] on the subject and volumes such as the present one.

2. FUNDAMENTALS

If a sample is irradiated with monochromatic photons of frequency ν, the photons may be absorbed resulting in the emission of electrons defined by the Einstein relation,[5]

$$h\nu = E_{BE} + E_K \qquad (1)$$

E_{BE} is the ionization energy or binding energy of the kth species of electron in the material, and E_K is the kinetic energy of the ejected electron. A photoelectron ejected from a free molecule will have lower kinetic energy due to vibrational and rotational energy imparted to the molecule by the photon. For solids, the vibrational and rotational terms are usually neglected, although Citrin et al.[6] found core photoelectron transitions in alkali halides exhibit temperature-dependent line widths consistent with excitation of lattice vibrations during photoemission. Including correction terms for the spectrometer work function ϕ_{sp} and sample charging ϕ_{sa}, Equation 1 becomes

$$h\nu = E_{BE} + E_K + \phi_{sp} + \phi_{sa} \qquad (2)$$

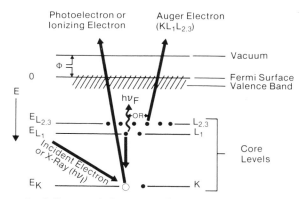

Figure 1. Energy level diagram of electron or photon excitation of an atom that results in photoionization and the subsequent relaxation that results in Auger electron or x-ray emission.

Assuming that the Fermi level of the sample and spectrometer align, the binding energy of any core level, as shown in Figure 1, is the energy separation between that core level and the Fermi level of the sample. For conductive samples in contact with an electron spectrometer, the Fermi levels of the sample and spectrometer will be coincident. As a result, the spectrometer work function can be determined by obtaining the spectrum of a conductive material with known binding energies. The instrument is adjusted until the binding energies agree with the known value. The spectrometer work function remains relatively constant. When the apparatus has been exposed to atmospheric pressure for maintenance or other purposes, a redetermination of ϕ_{sp} may be necessary.

For semiconductors and insulators the Fermi level lies somewhere between the filled valence band and empty conduction band. The Fermi level for semiconductors and insulators is obtained by determining the specimen work function using internal calibration or charge correction.[7] Internal calibration is accomplished by mixing or evaporating a conductive material with known binding energies onto the sample.

3. INSTRUMENTATION

3.1. Energy Analyzers

The kinetic energy of the ejected electron is measured using an electrostatic or magnetic analyzer. The function of the energy analyzer is to measure the number of photoelectrons as a function of their energy. Of all the analyzer designs, the double-pass cylindrical mirror and 180° spherical sector analyzer are among the

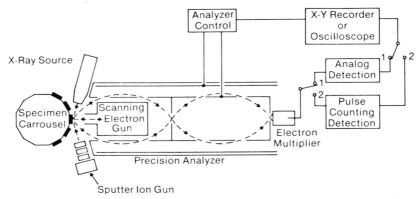

Figure 2. The geometry of a double-pass cylindrical mirror analyzer used for x-ray photoelectron spectroscopy.

most popular in commercial instrumentation. Figure 2 shows a schematic diagram of the double-pass cylindrical mirror analyzer. The analyzer consists of two stages of coaxial cylinders with a negative potential applied to the outer cylinder. The potential applied between the inner and outer cylinders creates a cylindrical retarding potential.[8] Electrons which leave the sample positioned at the focal point of the analyzer pass through an annular defining slit, then pass into the radial field between the cylinders to be focused back to the axis by the negative potential. The electrons pass into the second cylindrical mirror anlyzer to be focused onto an electron multiplier.

The use of tandem cylindrical capacitors improves energy resolution over a single-stage device. Energy resolution is also improved by first decelerating the electrons through the use of a retarding field formed by spherical grids at the entrance to the analyzer. If electrons leaving the sample with kinetic energy E_K are retarded to an energy E_0 for transmission through the analyzer, then the resolving power of the complete system will be improved by a factor equal to the retarding ratio, E_K/E_0. Retardation also gives rise to an improvement in sensitivity at a fixed energy resolution since a larger slit may be used at the lower transmission energies.

Retardation has been accomplished through the use of an electrostatic lens in conjunction with the 180° hemispherical analyzer shown schematically in Figure 3. The use of a lens focuses the electrons toward the acceptance angle of the analyzer. The use of an extracting and retarding lens also allows more variation in sample position due to its depth of focus. The hemispherical analyzer deflects the electrons 180° in the field between two concentric spheres. Electrons enter the analyzer near the center of the gap defined by a slit and exit after 180° deflection. Energy resolution is controlled by the radial source width, the axial

ELECTRON SPECTROMETER

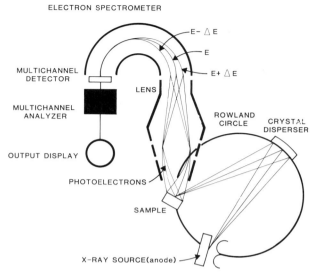

Figure 3. Schematic diagram of a 180° hemispherical analyzer with electrostatic lens.

source height, the detector width, the radial angle of emission, the axial angle of emission, and the optic circle radius.[9]

It is necessary to terminate the fringing fields at the entrance and exit to the electrodes of both the cylindrical (CMA) and hemispherical analyzers. Fringing fields at the ends of the CMA may be terminated by a series of rings coupled by dividing resistors or by resistively coated ceramic disks. The fringing fields of the hemispherical analyzer may be terminated by concentric wires or shaped electrodes biased at the electron pass energy.

3.2. Electron Detectors

The most commonly used detectors in XPS are channel electron multipliers.[10] These consist of lead-doped glass tubes with a semiconducting coating possessing a high secondary electron yield. A high voltage of a few kilovolts is applied between the ends of the multiplier to produce a gain of 10^6–10^8 due to the cascade of collisions as electrons travel down the inside of the tube. The detectors are frequently coiled to reduce noise due to ions produced in the multiplier. They have a high gain even for electrons at low kinetic energy and a low background count of less than 1 count per minute. The output of the multiplier is a series of pulses that are fed into a pulse amplifier–discriminator, then into a digital-to-analog converter, and stored in a multichannel analyzer or a computer.

Spherical and cylindrical sector spectrometers with a well-defined focal plane where electron energy can be related to position in the exit plane of the analyzer have been equipped with multiarray detectors. The exit slit is removed and replaced by a parallel array of multipliers. The sensitivity is increased, in principle, by the number of equivalent slits which would occupy the detector area.

A common configuration accelerates the electrons at 4–5 kV toward a phosphor that converts them into light pulses which are recorded with a Vidicon camera. The spatial location of the light pulses is correlated with electron energy. With this arrangement, a 10 eV or larger range can be detected simultaneously.

3.3. Magnetic Shielding

Electron spectrometers generally operate in the 0.01–0.20% resolution range, $\Delta E_K/E_K$. For high-resolution applications it is necessary to reduce the stray magnetic fields within the volume of the analyzer to a level of approximately 10^{-4} G (gauss). This is necessary since the path of the electron is perturbed by magnetic fields to an extent roughly equal to the dispersion of an electrostatic spectrometer. Quantitative estimates of the stray magnetic field limit for a given resolution may be calculated.[11] Magnetic field cancellation has been accomplished by using sets of Helmholtz coils[12] or ferromagnetic shielding.[13] Ferromagnetic shielding is used exclusively on commercial spectrometers because it is simple, compact, and less sensitive to magnetic field variations. Caution should be exercised since localized areas of magnetism can develop due to accidental blows to the shielding or by contact with strong magnetic fields. Degaussing with an RF (radio-frequency) coil after any activity that requires entering the analyzer housing is a common safety precaution. Shielding is accomplished by using two or more layers of commercially available ferromagnetic alloys (i.e., conetic or mumetal) whose permeability ratio is several orders of magnitude greater than iron.

3.4. Vacuum Systems

The vacuum system that is used must maintain a pressure so that photoelectrons have a long mean free path relative to the dimensions of the spectrometer and so that the partial pressure of residual gases will not contaminate the sample surface during the time of analysis. The requirement for a long electron mean free path is satisfied at pressures at 10^{-3} Pa or lower. The surface sensitivity of XPS requires total pressures of $\lesssim 10^{-7}$ Pa in order to permit adequate control of surface composition. The time to build up a monolayer of residual gas will depend on the pressure and the sticking coefficient of the gas. Adequate pressures can be achieved by a variety of techniques[14]; however, the most common system is a getter-ion pump complemented by a sublimation pump with a cryogenic shroud and sorption forepump. The vacuum system is of stainless steel construction with crushed metal gaskets. Using this approach, total pressures of 10^{-9} Pa can be achieved.

3.5. X-ray Source

Figure 2 shows the x-ray excitation source positioned in proximity to the sample and to the entrance to the analyzer to ensure the greatest solid angle between the x-ray anode and the sample and between the sample and the analyzer. The basic x-ray source includes a heated filament and a large target anode. Electrons from the filament are accelerated toward the anode to produce radiation that consists of a continuum of bremsstrahlung radiation with characteristic x-ray lines superimposed upon it. The continuum has a maximum energy that corresponds to the maximum energy of the bombarding electrons and a maximum intensity between one-half and two-thirds of the primary electron energy. The characteristic x-ray lines are a result of relaxation of atoms ionized during electron bombardment. During the relaxation process, electrons from an outer shell fill inner shell vacancies while simultaneously emitting an x-ray.

X-ray sources are constructed in a variety of ways. Figure 4 shows the basic

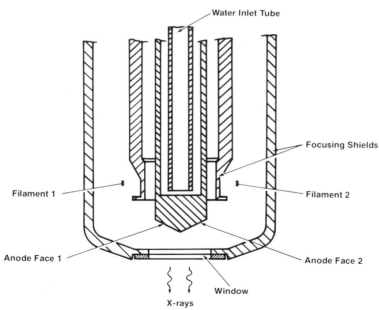

Figure 4.   X-ray source with dual filament and anode faces capable of separate x-ray excitation. (After A. Barrie, in *Handbook of X-ray and Ultraviolet Photoelectron Spectroscopy*, D. Briggs, Ed., Heyden, London, 1977, p. 83.

components of a dual anode x-ray source, which are basically the same as those of a single anode source. The anode is held at a high positive potential while the filament is held near ground potential.[15] The positive potential on the anode ensures that scattered electrons do not enter the sample chamber but are reattracted to the anode. The cooling water source that dissipates heat from the tip of the anode must be electrically isolated when the anode is operated at positive potential. The filaments are positioned out of line of sight of the anode to prevent the deposition of filament material on the anode target. Buildup of contamination on the target would significantly attenuate the number of x-rays emitted from the source. Independent operation of either filament can selectively excite either anode face.

The efficiency of x-ray production is only about one percent of the total applied power.[16] The actual intensity of x-rays produced depends on the voltage and current of the electron beam striking the anode. The threshold energy for the process is the binding energy of the inner shell electrons. The intensity of x-ray production just above threshold is very low but increases rapidly to a maximum some 5–10 times the threshold energy.

A thin, x-ray transmitting window separates the excitation region from the specimen. The window prevents the entry of scattered electrons from the x-ray source into the sample chamber. It also must attenuate high-energy bremsstrahlung radiation without greatly affecting the characteristic radiation. The actual window attenuation may be estimated from mass absorption coefficients.[17] The most common window materials are high-purity beryllium or aluminum foils.

Ideally the x-ray source will produce monochromatic radiation with sufficient energy to excite core electrons of all the elements in the periodic table. The anode materials most commonly utilized as the desired nearly monochromatic radiation sources are Mg and Al. The x-ray spectrum from these targets is dominated by a very intense $K\alpha_1$-$K\alpha_2$ doublet, resulting from $2p_{3/2} \to 1s$ and $2p_{1/2} \to 1s$ transitions. The $K\alpha_{1,2}$ doublet of Mg has an energy of 1253.6 eV with a line width (full width at half-maximum height, FWHM) of 0.7 eV.[18] The $K\alpha_{1,2}$ doublet of Al has an energy of 1486.6 eV with a FWHM of 0.8 eV.[19] The sources are not truly monochromatic but contain other less intense lines which are listed in Table 1. The $K\alpha'$, $K\alpha_3$, $K\alpha_4$, $K\alpha_5$, and $K\alpha_6$ transitions arise from $2p \to 1s$ transitions in multiply ionized atoms. An additional $K\beta$ band arises as a result of valence $\to 1s$ transitions. Each x-ray line will produce a set of photoelectron transitions in accordance with Equation 2. The sets of photoelectron transitions will be separated in energy by the energy separation of the x-ray lines. The intensities of the sets of photoelectron transitions will correspond to the relative intensity of the corresponding x-rays. Since the relative intensity and energy of the characteristic x-rays listed in Table 1 are known, the contribution of all but that due to the $AlK\alpha_{1,2}$ doublet may be subtracted from the XPS sepectrum through suitable software.

TABLE 1. Characteristic X-rays Produced from Al and Mg Sources[a]

	Mg		Al	
X-ray	Energy (eV)	Relative intensity	Energy (eV)	Relative intensity
$K\alpha_1$	1253.7	67⎫ 100.0	1486.7	67⎫ 100.0
$K\alpha_2$	1253.4	33⎭	1486.3	33⎭
$K\alpha'$	1258.2	1.0	1492.3	1.0
$K\alpha_3$	1262.1	9.2	1496.3	7.8
$K\alpha_4$	1263.7	5.1	1498.2	3.3
$K\alpha_5$	1271.0	0.8	1506.5	0.42
$K\alpha_6$	1274.2	0.5	1510.1	0.28
$K\beta$	1302.0	2.0	1557.0	2.0

[a]From M. O. Krause and J. G. Ferreira, *J. Phys.*, **B8**, 2007 (1975).

3.6. X-ray Monochromator

Another means of removing background produced by bremsstrahlung radiation and satellite peaks produced by the less intense characteristic x-ray transitions is through the use of an x-ray monochromator. X-ray monochromators for specific application to XPS have been constructed using the $10\bar{1}0$ planes of quartz to diffract AlKα radiation.[20] The first-order diffraction angle, according to the Bragg relation $N\lambda = 2d \sin \theta$ is 78.5° when AlKα x-rays of $\lambda = 8.3$ Å are diffracted off the $10\bar{1}0$ planes of quartz with $2d = 8.5$ Å. Unwanted radiation is suppressed, while the ultimate resolution is improved by selecting a narrow band of the AlKα$_{1,2}$ radiation through the use of the quartz monochromator. The theoretical limit is 0.16 eV[20] while the best actual resolution was 0.22 eV.[21] A more typical value for commercial instrumentation of 0.4 eV.[22]

Since only a small fraction of the incident radiation is reflected to the sample in crystal diffraction, the crystals are elastically bent or ground to the circumference of a Rowland circle. Bending focuses the x-rays to produce a high flux per unit area. More than one crystal can be used to increase the x-ray intensity if they are toroidally bent and arranged in the nondispersive plane of the Rowland circle.

The dispersion of a quartz crystal depends on the diameter of the Rowland circle and the finite width of the x-ray source. If a sharply focused electron beam is used to bombard the x-ray anode, a narrow x-ray energy spread will be focused on the Rowland circle. As the source size increases, the energy spread increases and is spatially distributed across the sample. The analyzer can be designed so that its dispersion is opposite but equal in magnitude to that of the monochromator.[23] In dispersion compensation the sample must be positioned at the Rowland circle, while in fine focusing rough or irregular surfaces can be examined without loss of resolution. Since a larger source size can dissipate more heat, it can be operated at higher power than can a fine focusing source. In order to dissipate more heat from a fine focusing source, rotating anodes have been developed that effectively multiply the anode area by the circumference of the circular anode.

3.7. Excitation Sources

For nonmonochromatized x-ray sources, the primary limitation of instrumental resolution is the natural line width of the radiation. Table 2 lists a variety of sources that have been investigated[13]; however, the most frequently used remain Al and Mg. Narrower sources are available since the FWHM decreases with decreasing atomic number as a result of a degrease in spin–orbit splitting or an increase in the lifetime of the hole. Although materials of lower atomic number have more favorable FWHM, they are not used because of their chemical reactivity, poor thermal conductivity, or high vapor pressure. Table 2 also lists anode materials with x-ray energies higher than Al. Use of these materials results in loss of resolution in an XPS spectrum. More information is gained when one of the higher energy sources is used because of the excitation of more tightly bound Auger electrons and photoelectrons. When more than one source is available, as in the case of a dual anode source, higher energy x-rays may be used to complement Mg or Al.

When only one source is available, Mg or Al offer the best combination of excitation, energy, and resolution. Even then, high energy Auger lines may be excited by bremsstrahlung radiation in the normal operation of an x-ray anode.[24]

TABLE 2. X-ray Photoelectron Excitation Sources

Radiation	Energy (eV)	Full width at half-maximum height (eV)
Y $M\zeta$	132.3	0.44
Zr $M\zeta$	151.4	0.77
Na $K\alpha$	1041.0	0.4
Mg $K\alpha$	1253.6	0.7
Al $K\alpha$	1486.6	0.8
Si $K\alpha$	1739.4	0.8
Ti $K\alpha_1$	4511	1.4
Cr $K\alpha_1$	5415	2.1
Cu $K\alpha_1$	8048	2.5

The bremsstrahlung radiation of an anode operated at 10 keV ranges from 2 to 10 keV with a minimum intensity at 4 keV.[25] The normal low bremsstrahlung intensity can be enhanced by substituting a Be foil window for the customary Al foil. Auger lines up to 2.5 keV can be conveniently recorded even when the characteristic x-ray energy is only 1.5 keV.

4. SPECTRAL FEATURES

4.1. Data Presentation

Figure 5 shows a typical XPS spectrum. The data is presented as intensity or count rate versus either kinetic energy or binding energy. The analyzer determines electron kinetic energy; therefore, a display of intensity versus binding energy requires correction for the x-ray energy according to Equation 1. The carbon spectrum in Figure 5 shows as intense C $1s$ transition due to $AlK\alpha_{1,2}$ radiation. At an energy separation of $\sim$10 eV on the low-binding-energy side of the main peak appear C $1s$ transitions due to $AlK\alpha_3$ and $AlK\alpha_4$ radiation. Features due to $AlK\alpha_{4,5}$ and AlK_β radiation are not visible without expanding the scale. The broad feature appearing at approximately 12 eV to the high-binding-energy side of the intense C $1s$ peak is due to inelastic scattering of the photoelectrons as they leave the solid.

Since the atomic structure of each element in the periodic table is distinct from all the others, measurement of the electron-binding energies permits identification of the presence of elements on the sample surface. The binding energies

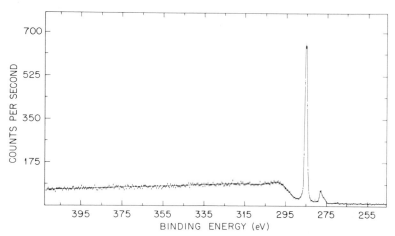

Figure 5. Carbon 1s photoelectron spectrum.

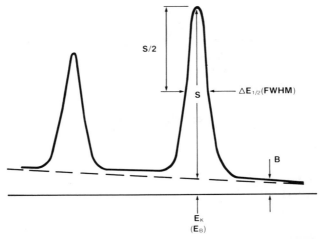

Figure 6. Silver $3d_{3/2}$ and $3d_{5/2}$ spectrum showing signal S, background B, and full line width at one-half of the maximum signal height (FWHM).

for the energy levels excited by Al or Mg radiation have been tabulated in a number of references.[1,26]

The curve that is recorded for an electron transition generally displays Lorentzian-type distribution, as shown in Figure 6. The background is the area under a line connecting points on the trace above and below the feature of interest. The signal intensity is determined by measuring the height of a line drawn vertically from the centroid of the peak to the background region or by measuring the area under the curve. The signal-to-noise ratio (S/N) is the signal in the peak relative to the noise measured at some point off the peak. The peak-to-peak noise represents the difference between the maximum and minimum fluctuations in the intensity at this point. The full width at half-maximum (FWHM) is the peak width at half the signal height. The measured FWHM E_M is a convolution of contributions from the photon source E_P, the electron energy analyzer E_A, and the natural line width of the atomic level E_N. The sum of the squares of these factors is the square of the measured FWHM:

$$\Delta E_M^2 = \Delta E_P^2 + \Delta E_A^2 + \Delta E_N^2 \tag{3}$$

Spin–orbit coupling results in splitting of the atomic p, d, and f energy levels into $p_{1/2}$ and $p_{3/2}$, $d_{3/2}$ and $d_{5/2}$, and $f_{5/2}$ and $f_{7/2}$ components. The magnitude of the splitting increases with increasing atomic number. When the splitting becomes large enough for the transitions to be resolved, separate binding energy values are tabulated for each peak.[26]

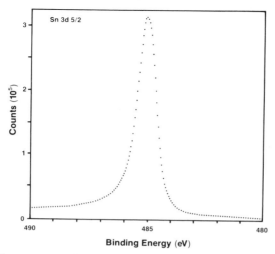

Figure 7. Tin $3d_{5/2}$ spectrum demonstrating the asymmetric line broadening observed in the photoelectron spectra of metallic samples.

4.2. Line Broadening

A number of electrical and chemical effects can change the Lorentzian shape of the peak. Lifetime broadening results in symmetric broadening of the peak. Asymmetric broadening occurs in metals as a result of the production of a positive potential site with a final state energy less than the original surface.[27] The positive potential scatters the conduction electrons across the Fermi energy level, providing a continuous range of allowed one-electron excitation energies. What is expected is an asymmetric tailing of the main peak to the high-binding-energy side, the extent of which depends on the density of states at the Fermi energy. A high density of states results in extensive asymmetric broadening and a general decrease in the intensity of the primary peak. Figure 7 shows the asymmetric broadening of the Sn $3d_{5/2}$ peak.

The overall intensity and structure of photoelectron transitions is also affected by plasmon excitation. The photoelectron passing through the crystal couples with its longitudinal electric field and electron density fluctuations to create extrinsic plasmons. In addition, the hole that is produced by photoemission creates intrinsic plasmons during its relaxation.[28]

A spectrum is composed of both extrinsic and intrinsic contributions. Figure 8 shows the Al $2s$ spectrum with its plasmon structure. This consists of the zero loss line and the plasmon structure which consists of a series of loss peaks spaced at even intervals with decreasing intensity. Plasmon loss peaks are not generally observed if the surface becomes oxidized. The free electrons in the conduction

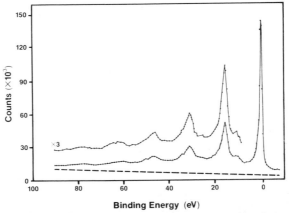

Figure 8. Aluminum 2s spectrum showing the zero loss line and its characteristic plasmon loss structure.

band that participate in the electron density fluctuations are involved in chemical bonding in the oxide.[29]

4.3. Chemical Effects

The primary strength of XPS is the ability to detect small changes in electron binding energy as a result chemical bonding effects. Figure 9 shows the Si 2p spectrum of a Si wafer with residual native oxide. The chemical shift of the Si 2p for the oxide is 4.5 eV. This is sufficient to easily identify the presence of SiO_2 on Si.

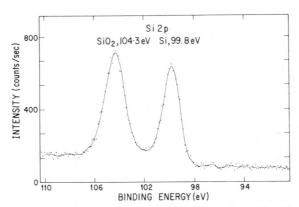

Figure 9. Photoelectron spectrum of a single crystalline wafer of Si with a native oxide. The Si 2p transition due to SiO_2 is shifted 4.5 eV from that of elemental Si.

When an atom occurs in more than one chemical form and the difference in the binding energies is smaller than the widths of the photoelectron peaks, it may be necessary to deconvolute the spectrum. Deconvolution is the resolution of the envelope that is produced when more than one chemical state is present into single peaks. This requires a knowledge of the line widths and peak shapes which may be determined in separate experiments. In all curve-matching exercises, the component peak heights, widths, and positions are adjusted until the calculated envelope matches the experimental one. There are many possible solutions, depending on the number and widths of the component peaks.

Deconvolution may also be achieved in the sense of removing the instrumental and excitation source contributions[30] identified in Equation 3. This is usually achieved by Fourier-transform techniques. Resolution enhancement using this approach approximates the natural line width of the peak.

There are other phenomena that may lead to multiple electronic states. These are manifested by the presence of additional peaks in the spectrum and loss of intensity in the zero loss transition. Shakeup and shakeoff are transitions of this type that are due to excitation of valence electrons when the primary photoelectron leaves the atom. Shakeup occurs when the valence electron is promoted to an unfilled higher energy level, while shakeoff occurs when the valence electron is promoted to the continuum. The resulting secondary peaks appear on the low-kinetic-energy side of the main photoelectron line due to loss of energy to the valance electrons.

Shakeup peaks contain chemical information due to the interaction of the photoelectron with the valence electrons. The chemical information content has been most widely studied for first row transition metals and their compounds. Copper and copper compounds are often used as examples because of the intense shakeup peaks associated primarily with copper in the +2 oxidation state.[31] The shakeup structure can readily be used to distinguish Cu_2O and CuO even though the chemical shift for the main core level photoelectron lines is small.

When there are one or more unpaired electrons in the valence shell, photoionization leads to more than one final state due to coupling of the unfilled shells.[32] The production of multiple final states is manifested by a splitting in the core and valence photoemission lines (multiplet splitting). The magnitude of the splitting is governed by the degree of exchange splitting, which is greatest when both electrons are in the same shell. The s levels are the easiest to study because they give rise to only two final states.

Figure 10 shows Mn 2s and Mn 3s transitions for MnF_2. Two final states, ^5S and ^7S, are expected as a result of photoemission from the s shell of a Mn^{2+} ion. The resulting multiplet splitting appears in both the Mn 2s and Mn 3s transitions. The splitting is greater for Mn 3s since the interaction is with the unpaired electrons in the 3d shell. Multiplet splitting of the p shell results in more complex spectra due to the greater number of possible final states.

Multiplet splitting, like shakeup, can be a measure of the bonding character of

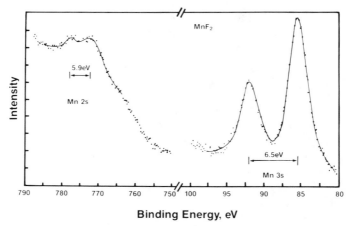

Binding Energy, eV

Figure 10. Photoelectron spectrum of the Mn $2s$ and $3s$ levels of MnF_2 showing multiplet splitting resulting from the coupling between the unpaired electrons left behind following photoionization and the unpaired electrons in the unfilled d shell.

the unfilled valence electrons. Systematic studies of multiplet splitting in transition metal compounds shows that the magnitude of splitting closely follows the number of unpaired spins.[33] A d^5 configuration would have the largest splitting. Decoupling occurs due to delocalization of the d electrons during chemical bonding. Also a strong ligand field splitting may result in pairing of the d electrons.

In addition to the photoelectron transitions, photoexcited Auger transitions are present which contain additional elemental and chemical information. Those Auger transitions that can be excited with either Al or Mg radiation have been tabulated.[26] The Auger transitions, like photoelectron transitions, undergo shifts as a result of chemical bonding. The Auger chemical shift is frequently larger than the photoelectron chemical shift. Wagner et al.[34] have shown that the chemical information in both Auger and photoelectron lines can be combined to provide a more definitive identification of chemical species. These author's have plotted the Auger peak position on the binding energy scale versus the photoelectron binding energy. The resulting plots distinguish chemical states that, in many cases, are not resolved in the photoelectron portion of the spectrum.

5. CONCLUSION

In general, the instrumentation for XPS has matured over the last decade. The basic nature of the photoelectron spectra is understood. Factors affecting photoelectron binding energies, peak shapes, and splitting are qualitatively and in some cases quantitatively understood. Standard reference spectra have been collected for data interpretation, yet a great deal of additional reference data is needed. Photoelectron spectroscopy has been applied to many different fields of study during the 1970s. In the years ahead, it will find increasing application in the area of surface analysis of materials.

REFERENCES

1. K. Siegbahn, C. Nordling, A. Fahlman, R. Nordberg, K. Hamerin, J. Hedman, G. Johansson, T. Bergmark, S. E. Karlsson, I. Lindgren, and B. Lindberg, *ESCA: Atomic, Molecular and Solid State Structure Studied by Means of Electron Spectroscopy,* Nova Acta Regiae Sci. Ups., Ser. IV, Vol. 20 (1967).

2. K. Siegbahn et al., *ESCA Applied to Free Molecules,* North-Holland Publs., Amsterdam, 1969.

3. D. W. Turner, C. Baker, A. D. Baker, and C. R. Brundle, *Molecular Photoelectron Spectroscopy,* Wiley–Interscience, New York, 1970.

4. D. A. Shirley, Ed., *Electron Spectroscopy: Proceedings of the International Conference on Electron Spectroscopy, Asilomar, California, Sept. 1971,* North-Holland Publs., Amsterdam, 1972.

5. A. Einstein, *Ann. Phys.,* **17**, 132 (1905).

6. P. H. Citrin, P. Eisenberger, and D. R. Hamann, *Phys. Rev. Lett.,* **33**, 965 (1974).

7. S. Evans, in *Handbook of X-ray and Ultraviolet Photoelectron Spectroscopy,* D. Briggs, Ed., Heyden, London, 1978, p. 121.

8. H. Z. Sar-el, *Rev. Sci. Instrum.,* **38**, 1210 (1967).

9. C. E. Kuyatt and J. A. Simpson, *Rev. Sci. Instrum.,* **38**, 103 (1967).

10. D. S. Evans, *Rev. Sci. Instrum.,* **36**, 375 (1965).

11. C. S. Fadley, R. N. Healey, J. M. Hollander, and C. E. Miner, *J. Appl. Phys.,* **43**, 1085 (1972).

12. J. H. Parry, in *Methods in Palaeomagnetism,* D. W. Collinson, K. M. Creer, and S. K. Runcorn, Eds., Elsevier, New York, 1967, pp. 551–567.

13. F. Wuilleumier and M. O. Krause, *Phys. Rev.,* **A10**, 242 (1974).

14. P. A. Redhead, J. P. Hobson, and E. V. Kornelson, *The Physical Basis of Ultrahigh Vacuum,* Chapman & Hall, London, 1968.

15. B. L. Henke, in *X-ray Optics and Microanalysis,* Academic Press, New York, 1963, p. 157.

16. M. Green and V. E. Cosslett, *Brit. J. Appl. Phys.,* **1**, 425 (1968).

17. B. L. Henke, R. White, and B. Lundberg, *J. Appl. Phys.,* **28**, 98 (1957).

18. M. O. Krause and J. G. Ferreira, *J. Phys.,* **B8**, 2007 (1975); M. S. Banna and D. A. Shirley, *J. Electron Spectr.,* **8**, 255 (1976).

19. E. Kallne and T. Aberg, *X-ray Spectr.,* **4**, 26 (1975).

20. H. Felner-Feldegg, U. Gelius, S. Wannberg, A. G. Nilsson, E. Basilier, and K. Seigbahn, *J. Electron Spectr.*, **5**, 643 (1974).

21. U. Gelius, S. Svenson, H. Siegbahn, E. Basilier, Al Faxalv, and K. Siegbahn, *Chem. Phys. Lett.*, **28**, 1 (1974).

22. Y. Baer, G. Busch, P. Cohn, *Rev. Sci. Instrum.*, **46**, 466 (1975).

23. K. Siegbahn, D. Hammond, H. Felner-Feldegg, and E. F. Barnett, *Science*, **176**, 245 (1972).

24. J. E. Castle and R. H. West, *J. Electron Spectr.*, **16**, 195 (1979).

25. C. D. Wagner and J. Ashley Taylor, *J. Electron Spectr.*, **20**, 83 (1980).

26. C. D. Wagner, W. M. Riggs, L. E. Davis, J. F. Moulder, and G. E. Muilenberg, *Handbook of X-ray Photoelectron Spectroscopy*, Perkin-Elmer Corporation, Physical Electronics Division, Eden Prairie, Minn., 1979.

27. S. Doniach and M. Sunjic, *J. Phys.*, **C3**, 285 (1970).

28. M. Sunjic and D. Sokcevic, *Solid State Commun.*, **15**, 165 (1974).

29. A. Barrie, *Chem. Phys. Lett.*, **19**, 109 (1973).

30. N. R. Beatham and A. F. Orchard, *J. Electron Spectr.*, **9**, 129 (1976).

31. D. C. Frost, A. Ishitani, and C. A. McDowell, *Mol. Phys.*, **24**, 861 (1972).

32. T. A. Carlson, J. C. Carver, and G. A. Vernon, *J. Chem. Phys.*, **62**, 932 (1975).

33. J. C. Carver, G. K. Schweitzer, and T. A. Carlson, *J. Chem. Phys.*, **57**, 973 (1972).

34. C. D. Wagner, L. H. Gale, and R. H. Raymond, *Anal. Chem.*, **51**, 466 (1979).

COMPARISON OF ESCA WITH OTHER SURFACE-ANALYSIS TECHNIQUES*

C. J. POWELL

Surface Science Division
National Bureau of Standards
Washington, D.C.

1. INTRODUCTION

Four techniques of surface analysis—Auger-electron spectroscopy (AES), x-ray photoelectron spectroscopy (XPS) [or electron spectroscopy for chemical analysis (ESCA)], secondary-ion mass spectroscopy (SIMS), and ion-scattering spectroscopy (ISS)—are being used to solve a wide variety of scientific and technical problems.[1] The purpose of this chapter is to summarize the principal features of

---

*Contribution of the National Bureau of Standards; not subject to copyright.

these four techniques and to compare and contrast the techniques on the basis of selected criteria.

A brief description of the four surface-analysis techniques is given in Section 2. Criteria by which these techniques can be compared are listed in Section 3; these criteria can also be used to compare different commercial instruments utilizing the same technique. Four of these criteria—spatial resolution; tradeoffs between spatial resolution, accuracy, sensitivity, and beam damage; qualitative analysis; and quantitative analysis—form the basis of a discussion of the relative merits of AES, XPS, SIMS, and ISS in Sections 4 to 7. Section 8 gives a summary of the principal advantages and disadvantages of the four techniques.

2. DESCRIPTION OF TECHNIQUES

The principles of AES, XPS, SIMS, and ISS, the relevant instrumentation, and the details of their application to different types of problems have been described in numerous recent review articles and books.[2-18] Further details of XPS and its applications are described in other chapters of this book.

Figure 1 illustrates schematically how each of the four surface-analysis techniques is utilized. The specimen of interest is inserted into a vacuum system (usually capable of ultimate pressures of 10^{-9} to 10^{-10} torr). The specimen is then bombarded by electrons (AES), x-rays (XPS), or ions (SIMS and ISS), and particles leaving the surface, either electrons (AES and XPS) or ions (SIMS and ISS), are detected.

For XPS, the specimen is bombarded by x-rays, often from a relatively simple x-ray tube. Characteristic x-rays from the x-ray tube anode (often Mg or Al) excite photoelectrons from core-electron levels (when energetically possible) of the specimen. The photoelectrons that emerge from the specimen surface in a particular direction enter an electron energy analyzer with which the photoelectron energy distribution can be measured. Peaks in this distribution correspond to photoelectrons from core levels that emerge without inelastic scattering in the specimen. The kinetic energies of photoelectrons contributing to these peaks are related to the core-level binding energies which can be used for elemental identi-

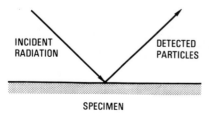

INCIDENT RADIATION

DETECTED PARTICLES

SPECIMEN

Figure 1. Schematic illustration of a surface-analysis measurement. The specimen is excited with incident radiation (electrons in AES, x-rays in XPS, and ions in SIMS and ISS) and particles leaving the sample (electrons in AES and XPS, and ions in SIMS and ISS) are either energy analyzed (AES, XPS, and ISS) or mass analyzed (SIMS).

fication.[2,17] The x-ray output of conventional x-ray tubes contains bremsstrah-lung radiation in addition to the characteristic x-rays. Photoelectron spectra with improved signal-to-background ratios can be obtained with the use of an x-ray monochromator albeit with a significant reduction of signal. The surface sensitiv-ity of XPS is due to the very short mean free paths (3–20 Å) of photoelectrons of energy between 100 and 1500 eV in most solids; those photoelectrons that are generated deep in the specimen have a much greater chance of being inelasti-cally scattered than those generated near the specimen surface and will not then be detected in the principal photoelectron peak.

With AES, it is usual to bombard the specimen with electrons of energy be-tween 3 and 10 keV to excite electrons from core levels. Core-level ionizations decay by one of two processes—the emission of characteristic x-rays or the emis-sion of Auger electrons. The Auger process is a two-electron decay process in which an electron from one level of the atom fills the initial core-level vacancy and another electron, either from the same level or another level, is emitted from the atom. The kinetic energy of the emitted electron, the Auger electron, is related to the binding energies of electrons in the level which was initially ionized and of the two electrons which participate in the Auger process. The kinetic energies of electrons emitted from the specimen are measured with an electron energy analyzer as in XPS. Peaks in this distribution correspond to Auger elec-trons that leave the specimen without inelastic scattering and with characteristic energies which are used to identify specific atoms.[2] As in XPS, the surface sensi-tivity of AES is due to the short inelastic mean free paths of Auger electrons in solids in the energy range of 30–2000 eV which is normally employed. Auger-electron peaks are also observed in XPS data where the core-level vacancies are created by x-rays. Use of electron beams for core-level ionization is attractive because of the greater "brightness" of electron sources compared to x-ray sources and because electron beams of small diameter can be easily produced.

SIMS is performed by bombarding the specimen by "primary" ions usually of energy between 5 and 20 keV. These ions collide with a succession of specimen atoms, and some of the specimen atoms are both ionized and have sufficient kinetic energy to leave the specimen; clusters of atoms also leave the specimen surface in an ionized state. These "secondary" ions are mass analyzed and detected. Information on the composition of the specimen surface can therefore be deduced from the recorded mass spectrum. The surface sensitivity of SIMS is due to the high cross sections for momentum exchange between the incoming primary ions and specimen atoms; higher surface sensitivity can be obtained with primary ions of lower energy although the secondary-ion yields will be lower. It is advantageous to detect both positive and negative secondary ions emitted from the specimen and also to be able to bombard the specimen with both posi-tive and negative ions to minimize the effects of large variations in elemental detection sensitivity that are encountered with use of a single charge state for either primary or secondary ions. Quadrupole mass analyzers are frequently used to obtain SIMS data, but mass analyzers of higher mass resolution (and cost) are desirable for distinguishing different fragment ions of the same nominal mass-to-charge ratio that may be present.

With ISS, the specimen is bombarded by 0.5 to 5.0 keV ions, usually of rare gases. Some of the incident ions are scattered elastically by the specimen, and those ions scattered in a particular direction are energy analyzed and detected. Unlike the secondary ions detected in SIMS, which are of low energy (most ions have energies less than 50 eV), the scattered primary ions have higher energies that are defined by the kinematics of the elastic scattering event, that is, the masses of the incident and target atoms and the scattering angle. The mass of a target atom in the specimen surface can therefore be deduced from the energy distribution of the scattered ions. Most of the detected ions of energy greater than 50 eV are associated with single scattering events, and the detected signal is therefore largely representative of the composition of the outermost atomic layer of the sample.

Ion bombardment of the specimen surface in SIMS and ISS leads to erosion of the specimen by the process of sputtering. These analysis techniques are therefore intrinsically destructive. Ion-beam sputtering is frequently used with AES and XPS to obtain composition data as a function of depth from the original surface (so-called depth profiles); depth profiles are similarly obtained in SIMS and ISS. Sputtering rates are, in general, a function of many parameters (masses of the target atoms, chemical composition, mass and energy of the incident ions, angle of incidence of the ion beam, among others).[19] Ion sputtering will thus in general lead to a modification of the composition of the specimen surface.

3. GENERAL CRITERIA FOR COMPARISON OF SURFACE-ANALYSIS TECHNIQUES

Any comparison or contrast of surface-analysis techniques must be based on appropriate criteria. We give here a listing of suitable criteria by which AES, XPS, SIMS, and ISS can be compared. Questions are raised concerning the types of problems that will be addressed, types of materials, and the nature of possible required measurements.

a. *Cost versus return on investment.* Central to the question of whether to purchase a particular instrument (or analytical service) is whether the anticipated benefits will exceed the cost. What also may be the cost of *not* making surface-analysis measurements? What are the relative merits of the purchase of a complete surface-analysis system and of purchasing additional components for an existing instrument?

b. *Nature, range, and number of specimens.* What is the nature (type of material, size, etc.) of the specimens to be analyzed? What range of specimens will be encountered and what are the analytical questions that are to be addressed? How many specimens are to be examined in a given period? What is the desired turnaround time from specimen receipt to insertion in the instrument, analysis, data analysis, and provision of a report?

c. *Analytical questions.* What is the purpose of the surface analysis? Is one looking for impurities, trace elements, segregants, or catalytic poisons? What is the problem to be solved? What are possible methods or techniques for the solution of the particular problem and what are their relative merits?

d. *Surface or interface analysis.* Is it desired to measure the composition of the outermost atomic layers of the specimen, some thin surface region of specified thickness, composition versus depth, or the composition and spatial extent of an interface? Will a destructive method for measurement of composition versus depth be required (e.g., ion sputtering, chemical removal, or mechanical removal) or can a nondestructive method be used (e.g., variable takeoff angle XPS and AES, Rutherford backscattering spectroscopy)?

e. *Spatial resolution.* What is the desired depth resolution (e.g., in a measurement of composition versus depth)? What is the desired transverse resolution (i.e., resolution in the plane of the surface)?

f. *Specimen homogeneity.* What is the spatial extent of composition inhomogeneities in the specimen, both parallel and normal to the specimen surface? Must the analytical technique be able to distinguish different surface phases?[20]

g. *Qualitative analysis.* Do all elements (including H and He) have to be detected? Is it likely that there could be interferences in the detected signals of major and minor constituents? What is the required sensitivity for the detection of trace species?

h. *Chemical information.* Is it important to determine the chemical environment of elements present in compounds? What is the valence state of a particular element? What is the nature of the chemical bond between different atoms?

i. *Quantitative analysis.* Is it desired to make quantitative measurements of relative elemental concentrations in the specimen? What accuracy is required? How much effort can be devoted to obtaining quantitative analyses?

j. *In situ processing.* Does the specimen have to be heated or cooled prior to or during analysis? Does the specimen have to be fractured? Does residual surface contamination (due to handling in the atmosphere prior to insertion in the instrument) have to be removed by sputtering or other means? Is it desired to modify the specimen surface (e.g., by chemical reactions, vapor deposition, sputtering, or exposure to a plasma) in the analysis chamber or in an ancillary sample-processing chamber?

k. *Other properties to be measured.* Does space have to be provided in the analysis chamber for the concurrent measurement of other specimen properties? Are these measurements compatible with the surface-analysis measurements?

l. *Automation and data analysis.* Particularly when a large number of specimens is to be analyzed or if a wide range of materials or problems is expected, the use of a surface-analysis instrument coupled to a computer can be advantageous for instrument setup, data acquisition and storage, data manipulation, data reduction, and data presentation. How comprehensive, convenient, and reliable is the computer system for the intended purposes? How easily can the hardware and software be upgraded in response to the availability of improved methods, techniques, or data?[20] What is the cost of a computer facility compared to the cost of manual methods.

m. *Specimen stability and vacuum requirements.* Will the specimen be damaged appreciably by electron, ion, or photon bombardment in the minimum time required for surface analysis? Will the intended specimens be stable in the ultrahigh-vacuum environment of most instruments? Will possible sublimation of specimen material cause later difficulty in operation of the instrument?

n. *Staffing.* Is suitable staff available to operate the instrument, to diagnose and possibly repair malfunctions, and to manipulate and interpret the data? How complex are the various instrumental functions?

The issues and questions raised above are not intended to be exhaustive. It is clear, however, that the selection of an optimum surface-analysis technique and instrument depends not only on intrinsic features of the technique but also on the specimen materials to be analyzed and the problems to be solved. In addition, solution of a problem will often require additional surface characterization (e.g., structure, roughness, surface area, electronic structure), bulk characterization (e.g., composition, crystal structure), or specimen processing (e.g., film deposition, reactivity).

Other chapters in this volume will show, by example, the utility of XPS or ESCA in the solution of different types of problems. The remainder of this chapter will focus on several of the above-listed criteria, permitting us to compare various features of AES, XPS, SIMS, and ISS.

4. SPATIAL RESOLUTION

The usefulness of surface-sensitive analysis is directly related to the actual or possible variation of composition with depth from the surface. The utility of any surface-analysis method depends therefore on its ability to detect particular surface phases[20] that may be present. A "surface phase" can be defined as that region of a specimen surface which has properties (e.g., composition) different from the bulk or another surface phase. Possible configurations of surface phases include atoms or molecules deposited on or segregated to a surface of another material, exposed grains of different bulk phases of an alloy, and an alloy or compound that has a surface composition different from the bulk composition.

The "information volume" of a specimen is that volume which gives rise to the detected signal.[20] It can be defined, in part, by the area of the specimen bombarded by the incident radiation, by the additional area illuminated by secondary radiation, and by the specimen area "viewed" by the analyzer. The information volume is defined also by the maximum depth from which the particular electrons or ions of interest originate. If the sample surface is being eroded by ion bombardment, the information volume will change with time. In practice, the information volume depends not only on the particular surface-analysis technique and instrument but also on the measurement conditions (particularly the takeoff angle) and the specimen material.

In any surface analysis, either qualitative or quantitative, it is important to determine whether a particular sample is homogeneous over the information volume from which information is derived. If more than one surface phase contributes to the observed signal, some ill-defined "average" surface composition will be measured. In such circumstances, it will be difficult or impossible to establish the accuracy of measurement. It is clear that the accuracy of measurement will be improved if the spatial resolution in the surface-analysis measurement is sufficient to detect separately the different surface phases on a specimen that may be present.

Table 1 shows the best transverse and depth resolutions of presently available AES, XPS, SIMS, and ISS instrumentation. A range of depth resolutions is shown to reflect the range of values of electron inelastic mean free paths in different materials for AES and XPS and different ion-sputtering rates for SIMS and ISS. As will be emphasized in the next section, the numbers in Table 1

TABLE 1. Lateral and Depth Resolutions for the
Surface-Analysis Techniques Indicated[a]

Technique	Lateral resolution (μm)	Depth resolution (Å)
AES	0.05	3–30
XPS	~1000	3–30
SIMS	1	3–30
ISS	100	~3

[a]For AES and XPS, the depth resolution is taken to be equal to the electron inelastic mean free path for the detected electrons. For SIMS and ISS, the depth resolution is related to the rate of specimen erosion by sputtering during the measurement time (see Section 4).

should be viewed in the context of the time required to make a measurement for a particular purpose and of possible optimizations of the measurement conditions. In fact, the numbers given in all of the tables presented herein should be regarded only as qualitative guides since many tradeoffs can and often must be made among the various parameters.

Of the four surface-analysis techniques, XPS has by far the poorest lateral resolution. Cazaux[21] has proposed and Hovland[22] has demonstrated a scanning-XPS system with which a spatial resolution of about 10 μm can be achieved with relatively thin (<100 μm) samples deposited on the Al anode/window of the x-ray source. Improvements in x-ray source technology may enable improvements of spatial resolution in XPS for other samples to be made in the future.[23] The best lateral resolution is obtained currently with AES. The best depth resolution (outermost-atomic-layer sensitivity) is realized with ISS. With SIMS, however, good depth resolution is obtained only at the expense of transverse resolution; high transverse resolution necessitates high ion incident current densities and rapid erosion of the specimen.

The current best transverse and depth resolutions indicate bounds on the information volume that can be probed with a particular technique. While knowledge of the bulk composition of a specimen and knowledge of its history may lead to useful inferences concerning the nature and extent of possible surface phases, it is recommended that tests be made for the presence of different surface phases whenever this can affect the interpretation of the surface analysis or the accuracy of analysis. Present commercial surface-analysis instrumentation gives only limited information concerning specimen morphology and homogeneity, but useful knowledge of the surface phases that may be present can often be deduced through variation of the available parameters.[20]

5. TRADEOFFS BETWEEN SPATIAL RESOLUTION, ACCURACY AND PRECISION OF ANALYSIS, SENSITIVITY, AND DAMAGE TO SAMPLE

Important tradeoffs have to be made between transverse resolution, depth resolution, accuracy and precision of analysis, sensitivity, damage to sample, and cost.[20] It is clear that additional sensitivity or precision in surface analysis cannot be obtained merely by increasing the time of observation (irrespective of the noise power spectrum) since the surface composition can change on exposure to the residual gases of the vacuum system and, in many situations, can be modified chemically by electron and ion bombardment. Also, the general presence of $1/f$ noise will limit improvements in precision which can be obtained by increasing the measurement time, as will the experimenter's patience or the cost of the measurements. Given then that the measurement time is limited, the experimenter will wish to develop a strategy appropriate for each type of specimen that will enable the maximum information to be obtained subject to the conflict-

TABLE 2. Beam Damage Effects for the Indicated Techniques

Technique	Beam damage
AES	Organics, glasses, adsorbates, some compounds
XPS	Adsorbates, some compounds
SIMS	"Dynamic" SIMS
ISS	"Dynamic" ISS

ing constraints of spatial resolution and sensitivity. Evans[9] and Werner[18] have shown graphically the tradeoffs that have to be made between sensitivity and transverse resolution for AES and SIMS. For SIMS, the sensitivity is also directly related to the sputtering rate for the particular specimen material and transverse resolution; there is consequently an inverse relation between sensitivity and depth resolution. Similar considerations apply to ISS.

Table 2 summarizes qualitatively the effects of specimen damage caused by the incident radiation for AES, XPS, SIMS, and ISS. Electron-beam-induced effects have been reviewed recently by van Oostrom[24] and by Pantano and Madey[25]; although the documentation of electron-induced processes and cross sections is meager, it is clear that beam-damage effects can be severe with organic materials, glasses, adsorbates, and some compounds. Theories for electron-induced mechanisms are currently under development.[26-28] Copperthwaite[29] has surveyed the nature of x-ray–induced damage in species under XPS conditions. Although some compounds, particularly ionic solids, and some adsorbates[25] are susceptible to damage by x-rays, the rate of damage is generally far less than those occurring under common measurement conditions in AES, ISS, and SIMS. The bombardment of specimens by 1–20 keV ions in SIMS and ISS is necessarily destructive. Data on ion sputtering rates has been summarized by Wehner.[19] The rate of ion-induced erosion of a sample is generally high under "dynamic" conditions of measurement (high transverse resolution and high ion current density) but can be made small under "static" conditions (low transverse resolution).[30] The nature of ion-induced damage (roughening, mixing, preferential sputtering, structure and chemical-state changes, diffusion, and implantation) have been discussed recently by Holloway and Bhattacharya.[30a]

6. QUALITATIVE ANALYSIS

Successful qualitative analysis of surfaces depends on the range of elements that can be detected, the elemental specificity in the analysis, elemental sensitivity, detection limits for a particular element, and the effect of the chemical matrix on the various spectra. These points will be discussed briefly in turn.

TABLE 3.   Elemental Range and Elemental Specificity
for the Indicated Techniques[a]

Technique	Elemental range	Elemental specificity
AES	Li–U	Good
XPS	Li–U	Good
SIMS	H–U	Good
ISS	Li–U	Small M/m good
		Large M/m poor

[a]The symbols M and m for ISS refer to the mass of the target atom and the mass of the projectile ion, respectively.

Table 3 shows the elemental range and elemental specificity for AES, XPS, SIMS, and ISS. For SIMS all elements can be detected, but for the other three techniques hydrogen and helium cannot be detected directly. Recent work has shown, however, that hydrogen incorporated in a lattice may modify the spectral lineshapes in AES and XPS associated with other elements. The elemental specificity for AES, XPS, and SIMS is generally good. This means that an element present in sufficient quantity can usually be detected; there are nevertheless circumstances where accidental overlaps and interferences can occur in the spectral features of two or more elements. For ISS, the elemental specificity is good if the ratio of the mass of a target atom to the mass of the incident ion is $\gtrsim 3$; if this ratio is $\lesssim 3$, it may be necessary to increase the mass of the projectile ions to resolve elements with nearly equal mass.

Table 4 shows the range of variation of elemental sensitivities and the variation of elemental detection limits through the periodic table. The variation of elemental sensitivities is approximately a factor of 10 to 20 for AES, XPS, and ISS but is considerably greater—a factor of about 10^5—for SIMS.[9,31-34] This range of

TABLE 4.   Approximate Elemental Sensitivity Variation and
Approximate Detection Limits for the Listed Techniques

Technique	Sensitivity variation	Detection limits (atomic fraction)
AES	Factor of 10	10^{-2}–10^{-3}
XPS	Factor of 10	10^{-2}–10^{-3}
SIMS	Factor of 10^5	10^{-3}–10^{-8}
ISS	Factor of 10	10^{-2}–10^{-3}

TABLE 5. Effects of Chemical Environment on Data Obtained by Each of the Listed Techniques

Technique	Effects of chemical environment
AES	Shifts in line positions; changes in lineshapes (particularly for core-valence-valence transitions)
XPS	Shifts in line psoitions; some changes in lineshapes
SIMS	Large changes in fragment patterns and in yields
ISS	Changes in yields

sensitivities is directly related to the range of detection limits in Table 4. Of the four techniques, SIMS offers the highest possible sensitivity for the detection of trace elements.

The effects of differing chemical environments on the observed spectra are summarized in Table 5. For XPS, in particular, small "chemical shifts" in the positions of spectral lines for elements are well documented and can provide useful chemical information. Variations in the difference in energy between photoelectron and Auger-electron features of an element in different chemical environments, as measured with XPS equipment, provide a useful diagnostic with insulating samples where measured binding energies and kinetic energies are affected by sample charging.[35] For AES, larger changes in line positions can occur with variation of chemical state than for XPS, although this is by no means always the case; chemical shifts in AES are not nearly as well documented as for XPS. Auger-electron features due to core-valence-valence transitions can show appreciable changes in lineshape with changes in chemical environment, but again the literature on these effects is sparse.[36] Some changes in XPS lineshapes (the asymmetry of the lines and the nature of "shakeup" satellites due to excitations of valence electrons) are also observed with change of chemical state.

Large changes (up to several orders of magnitude) in ion yields are observed in SIMS with change of chemical environment. Changes in relative ion yields from the same specimen, however, are much smaller (about an order of magnitude).[37] Appreciable changes in yields are found in ISS, but these are much smaller than those for SIMS. The large yield changes in ISS and SIMS are associated with variations of the neutralization probability of either the incident ion (in ISS) or a secondary ion (in SIMS) with chemical state. Variations of yield make quantitative analyses of surfaces difficult by these techniques unless the measurements can be made under carefully controlled conditions or there is knowledge of the relevant matrix effects.[37] Changes in chemical environment can also cause appreciable changes in the relative intensities of fragment ions and this information can be useful in identifications of chemical state (e.g., in measuring concentration profiles through a metal–metal oxide interface).

7. QUANTITATIVE ANALYSIS

Over the past few years there has been appreciable progress in the development of methods and data for quantitative surface analysis by AES, XPS, SIMS, and ISS. This progress has been reviewed and outstanding problems have been discussed in a recent article.[20] We will give here a brief discussion of three topics which affect the accuracy of analysis: the choice of analytical method, intensity measurement, and knowledge of the instrument response.

7.1. Analytical Methods

Three analytical methods are currently being used for quantitative surface analyses by AES, XPS, SIMS, and ISS. These are the use of local standards, elemental sensitivity factors, and an appropriate physical model.[20]

Local standards are the simplest means for making quantitative analyses. If analyses are required frequently of similar materials, the effort and expense of preparing local standards for comparisons of spectra (from the specimen and the reference) are warranted. Unfortunately, it can often be difficult to prepare a suitable standard of known composition and to ensure its stability and regenerability. The specimen and the reference also should have similar surface phases and topographies.

Elemental sensitivity factors enable a rapid and straightforward means of determining relative elemental concentrations on a routine basis. The accuracy of the analyses depends, however, on the absence of significant "matrix effects," that is, on errors associated with variations of parameters for elements in different chemical environments. As noted in the previous section, matrix effects in SIMS are appreciable. For AES, XPS, and ISS it is often convenient to use sensitivity factors to obtain even approximate values for the surface composition. It has been difficult, however, to estimate the magnitude of the likely error of analysis caused by the neglect of matrix effects, but recent work [37,38] has shown how corrections can be made for matrix and instrumental effects.

Relatively simple physical models have been developed for AES, XPS, SIMS, and ISS to describe the interaction of the incident radiation with the specimen, the generation and transport of electrons or ions, and the determination of the relative intensity of the emitted particles as a function of energy or mass. This approach to surface analysis is analogous to the widely used ZAF procedure in electron-probe microanalysis, where separate "corrections" are made for the atomic number of detected elements (Z), x-ray absorption in the specimen (A), and x-ray fluorescence (F). Physical models have not been used to a great extent for surface analyses due to the lack of needed data and to uncertainty about the validity of the particular models. This situation is changing. There is increased confidence now in the validity and utility of the physical models for XPS, in particular, and of the relevant data.[33,39] It seems likely that there will be similar developments for AES,[40] SIMS, and ISS. For the latter two techniques, a major remaining problem is to describe ion neutralization cross sections.

7.2. Intensity Measurements

The accuracy of a surface analysis can be no better than the accuracy in the determination of the relative intensities of detected electrons or ions. In general, the accuracy of the intensity measurement depends on the extent to which interferences can be minimized and the intensities associated with other processes can be subtracted.

Table 6 shows the factors which need to be considered in intensity measurements by AES, XPS, SIMS, and ISS.[20] There is still considerable uncertainty in identifying the correct area to be measured in AES, XPS, and ISS for all but the simplest cases, that is, symmetrical, well-separated features on a smooth background. At the present time, there are no accepted procedures in AES and XPS for background subtraction, correction for inelastic scattering, and identification of "shakeup" structures. Although deconvolution and background-subtraction techniques have been developed,[41] there are fundamental limits on the accuracy of this approach.[42] The spectra in SIMS are often complex due to the presence of molecular, fragment, and multiply charged ions. It is possible to detect and resolve intensities of ions of similar mass-to-charge ratios if the instrumental

Table 6. Factors to Be Considered in
Intensity Measurements with the
Indicated Techniques

Background:
  Multiple scattering (AES, XPS, ISS)
  Fragments (SIMS, ISS)
  Sputtering (ISS)
Source lineshapes (AES, XPS, ISS)
Inelastic scattering (AES, XPS, ISS)
Double scattering (ISS)

mass resolution is sufficiently high; for quadrupole mass analyses, the mass resolution is often inadequate for this purpose. The origin of complexities in ISS data have been reviewed recently by Baun.[43]

7.3. Instrument Response

Measured intensities in surface-analysis instrumentation depend on the electron- or ion-optical transmission characteristics of the particular energy or mass analyzer and on the efficiency of the particle detector. Ideally, these characteristics, together referred to as the instrument response, would be known functions of particle energy or mass. For some instruments, however, the instrument response is not well known, and this lack of knowledge has inhibited the transferability of raw data and results from one type of instrument to another.[20]

Although the instrument response may be known, at least approximately, for a particular type of instrument, there can be substantial variations in response from one instrument to another of the same type. Recent roundrobins that compare relative intensity measurements made under substantially identical conditions show variations of instrumental response of an order of magnitude or more.[37,44,45] A recent XPS roundrobin[44] showed order-of-magnitude variations in raw relative-intensity data for pure elements, but an analysis of the systematics indicated that the extreme variations were due to local instrumental artifacts or to operator mistakes. When these data were disregarded, there was still a factor-of-2 variation in relative-intensity data remaining. A similar AES roundrobin[45] has been conducted, and this also shows variations in relative intensities of over an order of magnitude; it was believed that the more extreme values of relative intensities were again associated with instrumental malfunctions or operator mistakes. Newbury and Heinrich reported variations in relative intensities of up to a factor of 50 in a SIMS roundrobin.[37] These roundrobins indicate that the major limitation on the accuracy of surface analysis now is appreciable variation of instrument response which can occur from one instrument to another. Until these variations are identified and brought under control (i.e., by the use of appropriate calibration and operating procedures), the accuracy of surface analyses will be suspect.

8. SUMMARY

A brief review has been given of features of AES, XPS, SIMS, and ISS that are important for qualitative and quantitative analyses of surfaces. Information given in the tables provides a simple, convenient, but *qualitative* means of comparing and contrasting the four surface-analysis techniques. As pointed out in

Section 5, significant tradeoffs can and often must be made among the various parameters (e.g., spatial resolution, sensitivity, beam damage to specimen) in order to solve a particular problem. The selection and use of a particular technique involves optimizations associated with the intrinsic capabilities of the technique and the particular instrument as well as extrinsic characteristics such as other physical and chemical properties of the specimen, as discussed in Section 3, and the nature of the problem to be solved.

The principal advantages and disadvantages of the four surface-analysis techniques can be summarized as follows:

XPS can provide presently unique information on the chemical state of an element. It is the technique in which least damage is done to the sample during analysis; this factor will, it is believed, become increasingly important as instrumental developments are made to improve sensitivity. Finally, XPS is the technique for which there has been most development in procedures and data for quantitative analysis. The principal limitation of XPS now is the rather poor spatial resolution.

AES is the technique with the highest available spatial resolution for the detection and characterization of different surface phases. This characteristic is extremely important in applications where submicrometer transverse resolution is essential (e.g., in the development of very-large-scale integrated circuits by the semiconductor industry). AES is a satisfactory surface-analysis technique for many applications, but its most important limitation is electron-beam damage to "fragile" specimens such as organics, glasses, adsorbates, and some compounds. The extent of electron-induced specimen modification needs to be better documented.

The principal advantages of SIMS are its ability to detect all elements and its extremely high sensitivity for the detection of some elements. The ability to perform microanalyses is also a positive feature of SIMS. SIMS, however, is intrinsically a destructive surface-analysis technique, and it is not possible to measure the identical sample a second time. Consideration therefore has to be given to possible alterations of the sample due to ion bombardment.[30a] Quantitative analysis by SIMS is particularly difficult on account of widely varying elemental ion yields in different chemical environments.

ISS is the technique which has the greatest intrinsic surface sensitivity. Its principal limitations are ion-induced damage to the specimen during analysis and matrix effects on ion yields. It should be emphasized that ion-beam damage effects in both SIMS and ISS can be made extremely small if transverse resolution is sacrificed; the same type of tradeoff can be made with AES.

The focus in this review has been on several specific intrinsic features of each of the four surface-analysis techniques and on factors which limit the reliability and accuracy of qualitative and quantitative surface analysis. There is growing recognition that the development and use of appropriate standards will enhance the analysis reliability and accuracy.[1,46] Use of standards will also improve efficiency in the use of surface-analysis equipment.

While all four surface analysis techniques give information on the surface composition of a specimen, each technique has different capabilities and limitations. It should be apparent that there is no "best" technique that is superior for all problems. As indicated in Section 3, the nature of the problem may indicate that one or other of the techniques is more likely to be successful than the others. Other chapters of this volume show the utility of XPS, in particular, for a wide range of problems. In practice, two or more surface-analysis techniques may often be required to characterize adequately the surface composition of a specimen and other forms of characterization may be needed to solve a particular scientific or technical problem.

REFERENCES

1. C. J. Powell, *Appl. Surface Sci.* **1**, 143 (1978).

2. A. W. Czanderna, Ed., *Methods of Surface Analysis*, Elsevier, New York, 1975.

3. P. F. Kane and G. B. Larrabee, Eds., *Characterization of Solid Surfaces*, Plenum Press, New York, 1974.

4. R. B. Anderson and P. T. Dawson, Eds., *Experimental Methods in Catalytic Research*, Vol. 3, Academic Press, New York, 1975.

5. H. Ibach, Ed., *Electron Spectroscopy for Surface Analysis*, Springer, New York, 1977.

6. L. -H. Lee, Ed., *Characterization of Metal and Polymer Surfaces*, Vols. I and II, Academic Press, New York, 1976.

7. J. W. Coburn and E. Kay, *CRC Crit. Rev. Solid State Sci.*, **4** (4), 561 (1974).

8. N. B. Hannay, Ed., *Treatise on Solid State Chemistry*, Vol. 6: *Surfaces*, Plenum Press, New York, 1976.

9. C. A. Evans, Jr., *Anal. Chem.*, **47**, 818A (1975).

10. R. E. Honig, *Thin Solid Films*, **31**, 89 (1976).

11. R. Vanselow and S. Y. Tong, Eds., *Chemistry and Physics of Solid Surfaces*, CRC Press, Cleveland, 1977.

12. S. R. Morrison, *The Chemical Physics of Surfaces*, Plenum Press, New York, 1977.

13. K. F. J. Heinrich and D. E. Newbury, Eds., *Secondary Ion Mass Spectrometry*, National Bureau of Standards Special Publication 427, Washington, D.C., 1975.

14. N. S. McIntyre, Ed., *Quantitative Surface Analysis of Materials*, Special

Technical Publication 643, American Society for Testing Materials, Philadelphia, 1978.

15. J. P. Thomas and A. Cachard, Eds., *Material Characterization Using Ion Beams,* Plenum Press, New York, 1978.

16. A. E. Morgan and H. W. Werner, *Phys. Scripta,* **18**, 451 (1978).

17. D. Briggs, Ed., *Handbook of X-ray and Ultraviolet Photoelectron Spectroscopy,* Heyden, London, 1977.

18. H. W. Werner, *Mikrochim. Acta,* Suppl. 8, 25 (1979).

19. G. K. Wehner, in *Methods of Surface Analysis,* H. W. Czanderna, Ed., Elsevier, New York, 1975, p. 5.

20. C. J. Powell, *App. Surface Sci.,* **4**, 492 (1980).

21. J. Cazaux, *Rev. Phys. Appl.,* **10**, 263 (1975).

22. C. T. Hovland, in *Proceedings of the Seventh International Vacuum Congress and the Third International Conference on Solid Surfaces, Vienna, 1977,* Vol. 3, R. Dobrozemsky et al., Eds. and publishers, p. 2363.

23. C. C. Chang, *J. Vac. Sci. Technol.,* **18**, 276 (1981).

24. A. van Oostrom, *Surface Sci.,* **89**, 615 (1979).

25. C. G. Pantano and T. E. Madey, *Appl. Surface Sci.,* **7**, 115 (1981).

26. M. L. Knotek and P. J. Feibelman, *Surface Sci.,* **90**, 78 (1979).

27. D. E. Ramaker, C. T. White, and J. S. Murday, *J. Vac. Sci. Technol.,* **18**, 748 (1981).

28. D. R. Jennison, J. A. Kelber, and R. R. Rye, *J. Vac. Sci. Technol.,* **18**, 466 (1981).

29. R. G. Copperthwaite, *Surface Interface Anal.,* **2**, 17 (1980).

30. A. Benninghoven, in *Chemistry and Physics of Solid Surfaces,* R. Vanselow and S. Y. Tong, Eds., CRC Press, Cleveland, 1977, p. 207.

30a. P. H. Holloway and R. S. Bhattacharya, *Surface Interface Anal.* **3**, 118 (1981).

31. L. E. Davis, N. C. McDonald, P. W. Palmberg, G. E. Riach, and R. E. Weber, *Handbook of Auger-Electron Spectroscopy,* 2nd ed., Physical Electronics Industries, Inc., Eden Prairie, Minn., 1976.

32. J. H. Scofield, *J. ElectronSpectr.,* **8**, 29 (1976); C. D. Wagner, L. E. Davis, M. V. Zeller, J. A. Taylor, R. H. Raymond, and L. H. Gale, *Surface Interface Anal.,* **3**, 211 (1981).

33. M. P. Seah, *Surface Interface Anal.,* **2**, 222 (1980).

34. H. A. Storms, K. F. Brown, and J. D. Stein, *Anal. Chem.,* **49**, 2023 (1977).

35. C. D. Wagner, D. A. Zatko, and R. H. Raymond, *Anal. Chem.,* **52**, 1445 (1980).

36. P. H. Holloway, T. E. Madey, C. T. Campbell, R. R. Rye, and J. E. Houston, *Surface Sci.,* **88**, 121 (1979).

37. D. E. Newbury and K. F. J. Heinrich, *Mikrochim. Acta,* Suppl. 8, 3 (1979).

38. P. M. Hall, J. M. Morabito, and D. K. Conley, *Surface Sci.,* **62**, 1 (1977).
39. C. J. Powell and P. E. Larson, *Appl. Surface Sci.,* **1**, 186 (1978).
40. C. J. Powell, *Amer. Lab.,* **10**, 17 (Apr. 1978).
41. H. H. Madden and J. E. Houston, *J. Appl. Phys.,* **47**, 3071 (1976).
42. J. A. D. Matthew and P. R. Underhill, *J. Electron Spectr.,* **14**, 371 (1978).
43. W. L. Baun, *Appl. Surface Sci.,* **1**, 81 (1977).
44. C. J. Powell, N. E. Erickson, and T. E. Madey, *J. Electron Spectr.,* **17**, 361 (1979).
45. C. J. Powell, N. E. Erickson, and T. E. Madey, *J. Electron Spectr.,* **25**, 87 (1982).
46. C. J. Powell, *Surface Interface Anal.,* **3**, 94 (1981); P. H. Holloway, *Surface Interface Anal.,* to be published.

CHAPTER

3

XPS ANALYSIS OF
SOLID STATE ELECTRON
DEVICE STRUCTURES

J. H. THOMAS III

RCA Laboratories
Princeton, New Jersey

1. INTRODUCTION

X-ray photoelectron spectroscopy (XPS), a surface-sensitive nondestructive measurement technique, is well suited to study the chemistry of surfaces and using appropriate depth profiling methods, can yield useful "chemical depth profiles"[1,2] by virtue of the strong "chemical shifts" in the binding energy of core-electrons levels due to chemical bonding.[3] XPS has been applied to many different areas of applied and basic research.[4,5] One very important area of application is the semiconductor industry.[6] Some of the recent applications of XPS to the understanding of solid state electron device structures will be reviewed in this chapter.

Three basic classes of solid state device structures have evolved over the past 30 years: semiconductor-semiconductor junctions, which are used as junction diodes, solar cells, junction field effect transistors, and bipolar transistors; metal-semiconductor junctions, which are used primarily as contacts, Schottky barrier field effect transistors (MESFET), and Schottky barrier diodes (solar cells); metal-insulator-semiconductor (MIS or MOS) junctions, which are used as, for example, varactors and insulated gate field effect transistors. Combinations of these various structures are used as the building blocks for active and passive devices and integrated circuits. The intrinsic or extrinsic chemical structure of the interface region between the metal and the semiconductor, or the insulator and the semiconductor in Schottky barrier devices and MIS devices, controls their electrical characteristics. For example, Schottky barriers or blocking contacts are formed when the work function of the metal is greater than the work function (electron affinity) of the semiconductor,[7,8] creating a space charge region in the semiconductor at or near the interface. Consequently, a potential energy barrier is formed. Band bending occurs in the semiconductor, and the Fermi level adjusts to be in thermodynamic equilibrium with the metal. The height of this barrier, $\Delta\phi$, is affected by the location of the Fermi level at the metal-semiconductor interface. Intrinsic or extrinsic states at the interface can trap charge carriers, causing the Fermi level to change position and therefore the barrier potential energy. Since conduction across the barrier depends on the barrier height, that is, $J \propto \exp(-\Delta\phi/kT)$, any changes in Fermi level position will strongly influence the junction conductivity.

The formation of a Schottky barrier is characterized by the barrier height, as just mentioned. The barrier height can be characterized by two quantities: the metal work function ϕ(metal) and the semiconductor electron affinity ϕ(semiconductor), such that $\Delta\phi_B = S\phi$(metal) + ϕ(semiconductor), where S is known as the interface index.[9] If S is large, the Schottky barrier height $\Delta\phi_B$ depends on the metal work function; and if S is small, the Fermi level is pinned and $\Delta\phi_B$ does not depend on the metal work function. In the case of material junctions, S is found to be small and the Fermi level is pinned. XPS studies have been oriented toward understanding the pinning phenomenon.

Similar phenomena are responsible for the electrical characteristics of MOS devices where emphasis is placed on the "surface" or channel conductivity of the silicon at the oxide–silicon interface beneath a control electrode (gate electrode). By varying the voltage applied to the gate relative to the substrate, the channel conductivity is controlled by moving charge carriers to and from the semiconductor–insulator interface. Here intrinsic states and defect centers act as charge carrier trapping sites and affect both C-V and I(channel)-V characteristics.[10] In general, these states are either directly or indirectly related to the microchemistry of the interfacial regions and consequently related to fabrication conditions, impurities, and the state of the semiconductor surface. Therefore, it is important to relate the measurable microchemistry at interfaces to device electrical properties.

2. PROFILING STRUCTURES

Chemical depth profiles as obtained by XPS involve the measurement of photoelectron peaks as a function of film thickness. This provides both elemental and chemical bonding information from the chemically shifted peaks as a function of depth. Functionally, this is accomplished by removing material from the device sequentially and performing XPS analysis of the newly exposed surface in a step-wise fashion. This technique is time consuming. The most common means of producing chemical depth profiles is by ion milling. This technique is widely ap-plied because of its compatibility with the ultrahigh-vacuum equipment that houses electron spectrometers. Films can be also removed by wet chemical etchants, gaseous etchants, or plasma etching. These techniques damage the material system. Nondestructive methods of obtaining chemical depth profiles include the use of angular resolved XPS and the sequential growth or deposition of materials of interest. The application of these techniques will be discussed in the remainder of this chapter.

The ion milling method of sequentially profiling layered structures has some inherent drawbacks since low-energy ions cause severe damage to the surface being investigated. Kim et al.[11], in an early XPS publication, showed that ions were capable of chemically reducing compounds having a low heat of formation. This point has been clearly demonstrated many times in various material systems. For example, hydroxides tend to be reduced to simple oxides. The ion beam may also create disorder within the ion penetration depth, that is, those events that modify bond angles but do not change surface chemistry. An interesting example is the SiO_2 layer on silicon—a relatively stable oxide that does not reduce under ion bombardment. Figure 1 shows the silicon $2p$ spectrum of an SiO_2 surface on Si as grown before and after ion bombardment (1 keV He$^+$) for 1 and 5 min. No appreciable sputtering occurred during this time. The silicon $2p$ line is broadened from 1.8 to 2.7 eV with no significant chemical shift. It has been recently demonstrated that the binding energy of the Si $2p$ peak is affected by the bond angle of the Si—O_4 tetrahedron.[12] In SiO_2, bond angles are normally distributed around 144°. The 1.8 eV FWHM represents a nondeconvolved view of this distribution. He$^+$ broadens this $2p$ peak. This broadening can be inter-preted in terms of a general increase in the concentration of Si bond angles above and below the average (144°).[13] Therefore, the broadening phenomenon is interpreted as an increase in the disorder at the SiO_2 surface. Further ion doses do not change the silicon $2p$ FWHM. In addition to chemical reduction or disorder-producing events, ion-induced mixing and subsequent compound forma-tion can occur due to ion knock-on cascade effects.[14-17] Such phenomena can occur over a considerable depth depending on the momentum transfer. Gener-ally, these phenomena can be minimized by operating at the *lowest* possible ion energy and by appropriately choosing the ion species to minimize chemical effects, ion-induced atom mixing preferential sputtering, ion penetration depth, and lattice damage. Even though the experiment may be well thought out, ion-induced atom mixing and subsequent chemical changes may be unavoidable. Therefore, other methods of sequentially removing material must be investigated. A number of useful reviews of ion-induced phenomena are available in the litera-ture (e.g., see Littmark and Hofer[18]) and so they will not be surveyed here.

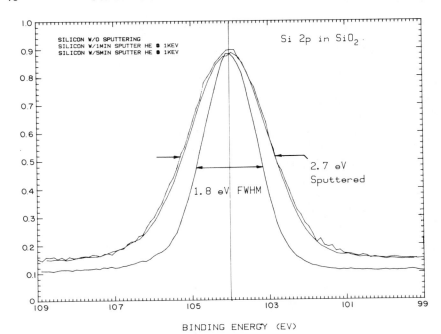

Figure 1. The effect of 1 keV He$^+$ ions on Si $2p$-oxide.

To circumvent the problem of ion damage and subsequent chemical modification of layered structures, a few novel approaches have been tried with some success. Grunthaner and colleagues[12,19] at the Jet Propulsion Laboratory, Pasadena, California, have used a chemical etch technique and a rapid sample introduction system attached to their spectrometer. In this way, wet chemical etchants can be chosen or manufactured to provide a uniform, relatively nondamaging etch-back medium. In a study of the SiO_2/Si interface, a preferred etchant solution of HF/ethanol was used. An NH_4OH/ethanol solution was used to study thin oxides on GaAs formed in a controlled environment. To date, Grunthaner's group is the only one to report the use of wet chemical methods in conjunction with XPS as a means of chemically depth profiling device structures. A 1000 Å thick SiO_2 layer [annealed thermal oxide (1100°C) on ⟨111⟩ Si] was chemically etched back to ~20 Å in commercial buffered HF. The resulting Si $2p$ spectrum is shown in Figure 2a. Note that the Si $2p$ line due to Si—O bonding has a FWHM of 1.8 eV similar to the Si $2p$ line before ion milling (see Figure 1). The BHF etch is clearly less damaging to the SiO_2 surface than ion milling. Although chemical etch-back methods produce less damage, they generally are not as universally applicable as ion milling.

Of more general application is the technique of angle resolved XPS, a totally nondestructive method of pseudoprofiling developed primarily in Fadley's

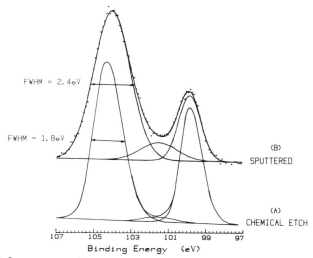

FWHM = 2.4eV

FWHM = 1.8eV

(B)
SPUTTERED

(A)
CHEMICAL ETCH

107   105   103   101   99   97

Binding Energy (eV)

Figure 2. Si 2p spectrum showing Si 2p-oxide, Si 2p-intermediate and Si 2p-substrate. (A) SiO$_2$ on Si (111) chemically etched back in BHF to 25 Å thickness. Si 2p-oxide FWHM = 1.8 eV as observed on nondamaged SiO$_2$ surfaces. (B) SiO$_2$ on Si sputtered to 25 Å thickness Ar$^+$ 1 keV.

laboratory.[20,21] Some elementary device structures consist of or can be purposefully fabricated with very thin overlayers on a substrate material, for example, Schottky barrier solar cells.[22] If the overlayer is thin enough, core-photoelectron lines can be observed directly through the overlayer. This occurs because of the finite escape depth of photoelectrons, λ, that depends on the photoelectron kinetic energy and to second order on the material system or matrix.[23,24] Useful "pseudodepth" profiles can be obtained using a photoelectron spectrometer with a small acceptance angle in the analyzer dispersive plane. Angle-resolved XPS is performed by varying the angle of the sample relative to the axis of analyzer slit. Photoelectron peak intensities depend on λ, that is, $I(PE) \propto \exp(-x/\lambda \cos\theta)$, where x is the distance from the sample surface and θ is the angle relative to the surface normal. This method is obviously limited to films with a thickness of the order of the escape depth.

3. SiO$_2$/Si

Because of its vast technical relevance,[25] one of the most studied device structures is SiO$_2$/Si. This material system has been characterized using the most modern analytical techniques. XPS studies have been most revealing. Electrical measurements (capacitance-voltage) performed on MOS capacitor structures indicate that electrical instabilities as shown in Figure 3 are in part related to

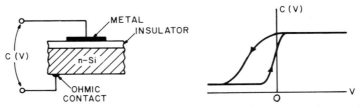

Figure 3. MOS capacitor and typical (*C-V*) characteristics showing electrical instabilities.

electrically active sites at the SiO_2/Si interface. The electrically active sites cause electrical instabilities by trapping charge carriers which create a space charge region that modifies the capacitance and semiconductor surface conductance. For instance, only one uncompensated "dangling" Si bond in 10^4 Si—O bonds at or near the interface is sufficient to produce the instabilities observed in a typical MOS capacitor structure.[26,27] This implies that the electrically active sites may be produced, in part, by intrinsic material defects which are due to the existence of a nonstoichiometric transition region from SiO_2 to Si. Surface analytical techniques are marginally sensitive enough to directly observe a defect atom or bond density of 1 in 10^4. However, it is likely that electrically active states may arise from a larger density of defect sites, most of which are electrically compensated.

In retrospect, physical models predict the existence of a transition region containing nonstoichiometric silicon oxide (SiO_x). Pantellides and Long's continuous random network analysis shows that SiO_2 can form directly on Si by simply deforming the Si—O bond angle within known experimentally verified physical limits.[28] This implies that the transition region is one atom layer thick. Other possibilities are also predicted by this model, including a finite SiO_x transition region. It is therefore reasonable that a transition region does exist and will account, in part, for observed electrical instabilities.

Two categories of XPS studies have evolved over the past decade: (1) studies of real device structures employing etch-back methods[12,19,29,30] and (2) studies of "thin" specially fabricated oxides or in situ oxide growth.[31-42] These classes are not necessarily directly correlated because, invariably, thin oxides are fabricated at low temperatures that may not have direct technological relevance (most device thermal oxides on silicon are grown at temperatures above 900°C). Both types of experiment do provide useful information aimed at the ultimate goal of characterizing the interfacial region.

The electron escape depth phenonomenon determines the sensitivity and maximum film thicknesses measureable in ultrathin oxide studies. As shown in Figure 2(B), the substrate silicon $2p$ line is observable through ~30 Å of SiO_2 and can be observed through a maximum of 100 Å. Therefore, the interface can be directly observed through thin layers without damaging the structure. The escape depth for Si $2p$ electrons at 1147 eV in elemental silicon appears to be well established at 2.3 nm. In the oxide,[12,30,38-41] the escape depth appears to be greater than in elemental silicon. Data range from 2.5 to 3.8 nm at 1147 eV and are in reasonable agreement with theoretically predicted values.[12,19,31-41]

Studies of the SiO$_2$/Si system have shown that the elemental Si $2p$ core photo-electron peak occurs at 99.4 eV relative to the Au $4f_{7/2}$ peak at 83.8 eV.[31-34] This peak position varies with substrate doping since measurements are refer-enced to the Fermi level. Clarke et al.[34] have shown that the Si $2p$ peak position in p-type silicon occurs at 98.9 eV and in n-type silicon at 99.9 eV and that the difference is the silicon band gap energy within experimental error (±0.1 eV). Band bending due to surface charge-up will also change the peak position. Silicon in SiO$_2$ is chemically shifted to 103.8 eV, an average of 4.4 eV above the ele-mental peak. The chemical shift for SiO is midway between SiO$_2$ and Si. Raider and Flitsch[31-33] have used the chemical shift to predict the stoichiometry of SiO$_x$, where $x = \Delta E_B/2.2$. High-resolution measurements by Grunthaner et al.[12,19] show that the chemical shift of the Si $2p$ line in SiO$_2$, Si$_2$O$_3$, and SiO are 4.6, 3.0, and 1.7 eV, respectively. The difference between these shifts and Raider and Flitsch's expression is due to reference energy shifts caused by band bending at the interface.

Hattori and Nishina[29] used 1.5 keV Ar$^+$ ions to sequentially remove 800°C thermal oxides on Si through the SiO$_2$/Si interface. Their analysis shows an interfacial nonstoichiometric oxide (SiO$_x$) of about 20 Å thick. Their model did not include ion-mixing phenomena. A theoretical prediction (LSS theory) of the ion range of 1 keV Ar$^+$ into SiO$_2$ or Si is 24 Å. If ion-induced mixing occurs over this range, a 20 Å interface width should obtain and is consistent with an abrupt interface broadened by ion-induced mixing within the ion range. In addi-tion to ion-induced mixing, new oxidation states are created due to bond break-age. Using 500 eV Ar$^+$, Grunthaner and Maserjian[19] have shown that as little as a monolayer ion dose produces severe ion damage. This is consistent with results summarized in Figure 1. Figure 2(B) shows a Si $2p$ spectrum after sputtering away 75 Å of a 100 Å SiO$_2$ film on Si with 1 keV Ar$^+$. Note the large intermedi-ate state amplitude. Comparing Figure 2(B) with Figure 2(A), the chemically thinned oxide sample, the effect of ion-beam damage to the interface is obvious. Grunthaner and Maserjian show evidence that the anomalous growth of the intermediate state is consistent with hot Si reactions at the interface and gives rise to chemical shifts that correlate with color centers produced in bulk silica and quartz.

As mentioned earlier, Grunthaner et al.[12,19] used a chemical etch-back method to study the SiO$_2$/Si interface up to the silicon substrate since HF does not effectively etch bulk Si. Although this method is less destructive than ion milling, the etch rate is affected by changes in oxide stoichiometry especially near the interface. This results in a nonuniform depth scale. From these results, these in-vestigators determined the interface width to be less than one atom layer in thickness.

In 1975, Clarke et al.[34] published results of an XPS study of thin wet and dry oxidized silicon. A considerable difference was observed in the ratio of oxidized to total silicon versus ellipsometrically determined SiO_2 film thickness. They attribute this to the possible existence of H_2O or OH in the interfacial region. A continuous change in stoichiometry was noted in the first 20 Å from the silicon surface. Hollinger et al.[35-37] estimated the interfacial region at 3 Å for oxides grown at 750°C and 6 Å at 25°C, indicating a possible interface dependence on oxidation temperature. Raider and Flitsch[31-33] studied ultrathin oxides grown at temperatures from 25°C to 850°C in various doped oxygen ambients. Ambient doping and 850°C thermal annealing was shown to have no significant effect on the interface width within experimental error. They noted that the interface width of oxides grown on (111) silicon is greater than the interface width on (100) silicon. The density of unoxidized Si bonds is estimated to be 1.8 times larger on (111) oriented silicon (1.4×10^{15} bonds/cm^2) and is consistent with the observed interface width. The interfacial region appears to be continuously graded in stoichiometry, as Hollinger et al. had found. Both studies employed ultrathin SiO_2 on Si grown at various temperatures. Therefore, it is not surprising that their results are qualitatively similar. In fact, it is possible that the graded nature of the interface stoichiometry may be due to the difference in low and high temperature oxidation.

Two-angle resolved XPS studies aimed at characterizing the interfacial region have been reported.[39-41] Iwata and Ishizaka[38] and Ishizaka et al.[39] studied ultrathin oxides grown at low temperature (550–900°C) on (100) Si. In this thickness regime (<1.0 nm), the interfacial region is directly observed and was deconvolved from the Si^{4+} and Si^0 2p spectrum. In these studies, the angle was varied from 21° to 81° with respect to the spectrometer axis. An example of ~10 Å SiO_2 on Si is shown in Figure 4 for 0° and 80-80°. The investigators' results indicate an interfacial suboxide species some 2–3 Å thick. The interface does not appear to be graded according to their analysis. This result appears to support the interpretation that interface studies based on oxides grown at various temperatures should not be used to "profile" the interfacial region.

To summarize, a great deal of information has been acquired regarding the SiO_2/Si interface structure and chemistry. An interfacial region of 1 monolayer (<6 Å) of silicon suboxide Si_2O, SiO, and Si_2O_3 is observed on thermally grown samples. Details of this region depend on growth conditions and substrate orientation. The application of mathematical Fourier deconvolution methods (resolution-enhanced XPS) to the Si 2p and O 1s spectrum resulted in a refined view of the SiO_2/Si interface. Near the interface, Si atoms tetrahedrally coordinated to oxygen have been shown to consist of 4-, 6-, and higher-order member $SiO_{4/2}$ rings, which correspond to Si—O bond angles of 120°, 144°, and >150°, respectively. As the Si surface is approached, the Si—O bond becomes more strained and consists of mostly fourth-order member rings (<120° bond angle). These results are summarized diagrammatically in Figure 5, showing the expected

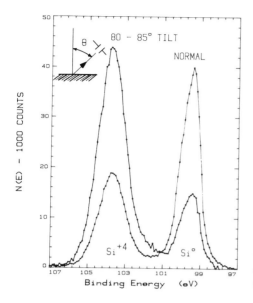

Figure 4. Angle-resolved XPS applied to ~10 Å SiO_2 on Si at 0° and 80–85° relative to the spectrometer slit.

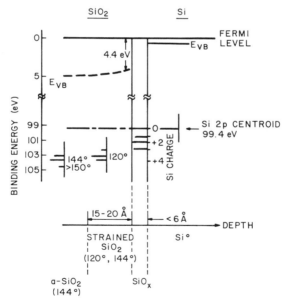

Figure 5. Interface of SiO_2 on Si showing the Si $2p$ and valence band. Binding energy is referenced to the Fermi level. Bent bond angle states and intermediate states are shown as a function of depth into the oxide.

45

variation in shape and binding energy of the Si $2p$ core level. The valence band is also sketched from Goodman's data for completeness.[43] XPS investigations are in agreement on the absolute centroid chemical shift of 4.5 ± 0.1 eV of the Si $2p$ line of SiO_2 relative to elemental silicon. Strained bonds account for a chemical shift of ~ 1.9 eV centered around the Si $2p$ line in SiO_2 and are clearly distinguishable from the suboxides.[44] Grunthaner and colleagues[19,44] showed that the states arising from the strained region in SiO_2 may in part account for some of the charge carrier trapping at the interface. The detailed picture of the SiO_2/Si interface by XPS is in general agreement with measurements by other techniques.[45-47]

4.   OTHER SILICON DEVICE STRUCTURES

XPS does not have good lateral resolution. Therefore, application of the technique is limited to large-area or simplified device structures. This category of devices includes Schottky barrier solar cell structures. Such devices consist of a metal–very thin insulator–silicon junction, as shown in Figure 6. The thin insulator provides the barrier.

Bachrach and Bauer,[48] using the Stanford synchrotron storage ring light source

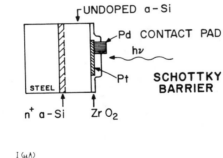

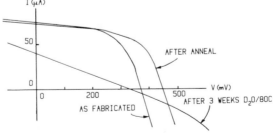

Figure 6. Hydrogenated amorphous silicon Schottky barrier solar cell using Pd counter-electrodes. Typical I–V characteristics are shown as an inset.

(SSRL) and soft-x-ray photoelectron spectroscopy (SXPS), studied the formation of a number of metal–semiconductor Schottky barrier systems by depositing thin-metal layers sequentially on well-characterized surfaces. The photon energy of the source is tuned to provide a minimum escape depth for the particular material system being studied. Aluminum on silicon is a common contact system for silicon devices and can form a Schottky barrier contact. When Al is deposited on thin SiO_2, Al reduces SiO_2 resulting in the formation of an Al_2O_3 interfacial layer a few atom layers thick and a silicon rich region under the Al_2O_3. Interface film thicknesses were not reported in detail. However, the thin SiO_2 layer under the Al_2O_3:Al/Si-rich region remains generally intact. Apparently, Al contacts on oxidized Si surfaces can produce complex junctions.

Another interesting example of device structural characterization has recently been reported by Thomas and Carlson.[49] Palladium on hydrogenated amorphous silicon has been tested as a model Schottky barrier solar cell structure (Figure 6). Devices perform well as long as they are not exposed to high relative humidity ambients. High relative humidity exposure causes a dramatic change in the diode current–voltage characteristics.[50] To characterize this phenomenon, XPS used in conjunction with ion milling was employed to profile through a Pd(100 Å)/a-Si:H structure. High-resolution spectra of the Pd $3d$, O $1s$ and Si $2p$ photoelectron lines were obtained as a function of sputter time. Near the interface, a structure was observed in the Pd $3d$ lines as shown in Figure 7. The structure is attributed to Pd in palladium silicide. Structure in the Si $2p$ was also observed. Upon deconvolution, chemical profiles of the chemically shifted Pd and Si lines were

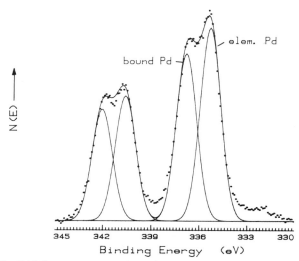

Figure 7. Pd $3d$ spectrum (on a-Si:H) after sputtering 15 min with 1 keV Ar+.

computed from the data. Ideally, this process should provide a very complete and detailed picture of the Pd/a-Si:H junction.

It was mentioned earlier that Hattori and Nishina's study was hindered by ion-induced mixing effects.[29] In the case of Pd/a-Si:H, the ion-mixing phenomenon is even more severe. Studies by Rutherford backscattering have shown that ion milling of Pt or Pd on silicon causes total mixing within the ion penetration depth and produces stoichiometric silicides in this range.[14-17] Using a simple model for mixing based on RBS results, Thomas and Carlson show that most if not all the Pd_xSi observed is due to ion mixing within the ion range.[49] Pd/a-Si:H XPS analysis using ion milling is an extreme case of ion mixing and compound formation obscuring useful data.

Even in the presence of severe ion mixing, some interesting features of the device structure were discernible. First, exposure of thin Pd/a-Si:H structures to high relative humidity ambients causes an increase in the thickness of the interfacial oxide. This is responsible for device electrical characteristic degradation. Second, it was shown that palladium appears to diffuse into a-Si:H at a slightly elevated temperature (80°C). Palladium silicide was also observed at the interface in concentrations greater than that expected from ion mixing. Obviously, more work is required in this area to enable us to fully understand these device structures.

SIPOS (semi-insulating polycrystalline silicon) is used as part of SOGO (SIPOS-oxide-glass-oxide) passivation of high-voltage-power transistors, as shown in Figure 8. SIPOS, which is typically deposited by chemical vapor deposition methods and forms the base layer of SOGO passivation, has been the subject of a

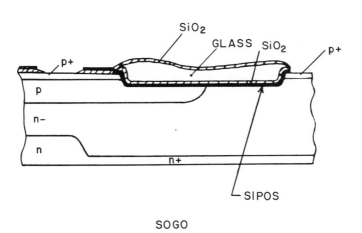

SOGO

Figure 8. SIPOS-Oxide-Glass-Oxide (SOGO) passivation on a typical high-voltage-power transistor.

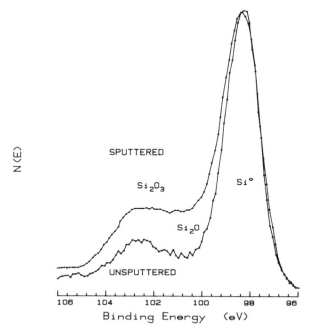

Figure 9. Silcon $2p$ spectrum for SIPOS $\gamma = 0.25$ annealed at 900°C in N_2. The effect of sputtering with 1 keV Ar^+ is also shown.

number of investigations aimed at understanding the microchemical composition.[51,52] Hamasaki et al.,[51] in a fairly complete study of SIPOS properties, showed preliminary XPS results which were used to develop a physical model for SIPOS. Silicon was observed to be bound to oxygen in what was interpreted as suboxides (Si_2O_3, SiO, etc.) from the structure of the Si $2p$ spectrum. Thomas and Goodman[52] showed that the high-binding-energy structure accounts quantitatively for the oxygen present for oxygen doping ratios ($\gamma \equiv N_2O/SiH_4$) from 0.05 through 0.40 in the deposition chamber. The silicon $2p$ spectrum, as shown Figure 9, was interpreted in the context of a more refined model for low γ material annealed at 900°C. SIPOS consists of silicon grains surrounded by Si_2O. The Si_2O is in turn covered with Si_2O_3. More recently, Adachi and Helms[53] have shown that for $\gamma = 3.1$ the material, after annealing at a high temperature (1100°C), consists of a large amount of SiO_2. Studies of SIPOS composition as a function of annealing temperature shows that the concentration of SiO_2 in SIPOS increases with annealing temperature and γ. Low γ material ($\gamma = 0.2$) normally used in device passivation layers remains predominately Si_2O_3 after annealing, supporting Thomas and Goodman's physical model.

Again, ion-milling phenomena (mixing and damage) were observed in SIPOS (Figure 9). Thomas and Goodman show that, after sputtering, the Si $2p$ structure is significantly modified.[52] The peak due to Si_2O_3 remains more or less constant, but the Si_2O peak increases in amplitude with ion dose. This is a direct indication of bond breakage and chemical reduction in the Si_2O_3 layer due to ion damage.

5. III–V COMPOUND SEMICONDUCTOR DEVICES

III–V compound semiconductors have been used for a long time in microwave device technology. The understanding of MOS field effect devices based on III–V compound semiconductors has advanced considerably in the past several years. However, native-oxide-based MOS devices are not presently marketed. Device structures, such as bipolar transistors, p–n junctions and Schottky barrier devices based on III–V compound semiconductors are used extensively in the microwave electronics industry.[54] Recently, synchrotron excited x-ray photoelectron spectroscopy has been applied to the study of Schottky barrier formation and oxide behavior on III–V materials.[48,55-59] A large percentage of this and related work is presented at the Annual Conferences on the Physics of Compound Semiconductor Interfaces, the proceedings of which are published by the American Vacuum Society. These studies are fundamental in nature and for the most part involve film buildup or growth rather than device structures in which material (oxides or metal) must be removed to study the interfacial region. The remainder of this chapter will be devoted to reviewing some important results regarding Schottky barrier and oxide formation on clean single crystal material surfaces, XPS characterization of oxides on III–V semiconductors, and finally a few words regarding ion milling and chemical etch-back methods applied to oxides on GaAs.

Lindau et al.[56] have shown experimentally (using SXPS) that metals deposited on very clean GaAs, for example, interact with the surface atoms and reorder the surface chemical composition. Similar studies were also performed on oxygen chemisorption on cleaved (110) GaAs surfaces.[55-59] Gold on GaSb forms a pinned Schottky barrier (S is small).[59] In deposition studies, the Sb $4d$ line is observed on the Au surface (see Figure 10) even after depositing enough Au to fully mask Sb at the interface. These studies have lead to the conclusion that Sb diffuses through the metal overlayer as the film is being deposited. A general model was developed that describes this process and the subsequent pinning of the Fermi level by extrinsic states created by this process. Spicer's model in essence states that the evaporated metal atom gives up its heat of condensation (~80 kcal/mol), which is large enough to break the GaAs covalent bond (~17 kcal/mol heat of formation as reported in reference 59). This allows surface atoms during deposition to become mobile and forms both cation and anion voids at the interface. The voids and local excesses create electronic states in the

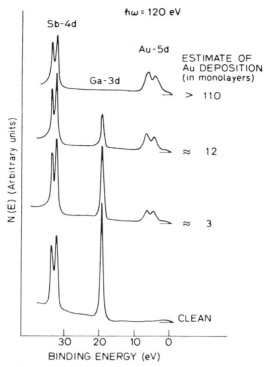

Figure 10. Ga $4d$, Sb $4d$, and Au $5d$ spectrum as a function of Au coverage. (Reproduced from reference 55 with permission of the copyright owner.)

forbidden gap of the semiconductor that pin the Fermi level. Not all III–V compound semiconductors behave in the same fashion, that is, S is related to the semiconductor heat of formation. Brillson[60] generalizes this concept to include the class of materials in which the deposited metal chemically reacts with the semiconductor surface. An example of chemical and structural changes at the interface is the Al/GaAs contact.[48] Al reacts chemically with the GaAs surface, forming AlAs in a replacement reaction similar to that of Al on Si contacts. In this case an interfacial layer of AlAs, which provides a different potential barrier height, is formed under the Al contact metal. In general, these phenomena account for the discrepancy between measured versus theoretically predicted barrier heights on III–V semiconductors. Brillson compared metals that react with GaAs with a nonreactive metal such as Au (as studied by Lindau et al.[56]) and was able to generalize Spicer's concept to include chemical effects on barrier height as related to the metal work function and heat of formation.

A large volume of experimental and theoretical research has been performed on III–V Schottky barrier formation. In addition, MBE has been used by a few groups to fabricate novel contact systems on III–V semiconductors (e.g., see Grant et al.[61]). Schottky barrier interfaces appear to be diffuse and strongly related to the volatility or heat of formation of the semiconductor surface. In film buildup studies, nonreactive species on, for example, GaAs form interfacial graded regions tens to hundreds of monolayers thick. Reactive species such as Al on GaAs form a relatively diffuse interface in addition to a region of modified chemistry, AlAs, a few monolayers thick (~6 Å). Actual device structures have not been much studied because of the complications involved in etchback procedures (ion milling or chemical).

Up to this point, the subject of III–V MOS device structures has not been discussed. Pianetta et al.[55,62] showed that oxygen reacts with GaAs surfaces and produces an effect similar to metal deposition; that is, extrinsic electronic states due to As vacancies are formed and pin the Fermi level.[63] Native oxides (thermal and anodic) are inhomogeneous, hygrosopic, and physically soft, and characterization of thick device-like structures is still in its infancy.[54] XPS studies are few in number.

The oxidation states of Ga, As, and oxides on GaAs have been determined from the chemical shift of both $3d$ and, when possible, the $2p$ photoelectron lines using Al$K\alpha$ x-ray excitation. This has proven to be a formidable task since GaAs tends to be insulating. Mizokawa et al.[64] used carbon contamination and, when it did not react with the surface, Au $4f_{7/2}$. Wilmsen et al. used the $2p$ lines relative to the $2p$ lines of a clean GaAs surface. Schwartz et al.[65] used a cleaved (110) GaAs surface as a reference and measured various oxide containing films and powders of Ga and As.

Wilmsen et al.[66,67] have studied the chemistry of thermal and anodic oxides of 25- to 500-Å thickness on GaAs and InP. In their studies, ion milling was used to obtain chemical depth profiles of these structures. As an aside, we should note that Honig and Magee[1] have demonstrated that ion-induced mixing in In$_x$Ga$_{1-x}$As/GaAs junctions is minimal and is basically equal to the ion range at the interface. Since the native oxides on GaAs are similar to the substrate in mass, it is likely that ion mixing in this case will be minimal. Therefore, to first order, depth profiles need not be corrected for ion-induced mixing.

Typical chemical depth profiles of a low temperature thermal and an anodic oxide on GaAs are shown in Figure 11a,b. Wilmsen et al.[66] used the Ga $2p_{3/2}$, As $2p_{3/2}$ and Ga LMM Auger transition excited with Al$K\alpha$ x-rays. Excess As is indicated at the interface of the thermal oxide but not the anodic oxide. The dominant oxide formed thermally is Ga_2O_3 with a residue of As_2O_3 and possibly Ga_2O. The interface is ~40 Å thick. Anodic oxides and plasma oxides (not shown) are mixtures of As_2O_3 and Ga_2O_3. The interface consists of a thin layer of Ga_2O_3 (30–40 Å), as indicated by the small excess of Ga_2O_3 and no free As.

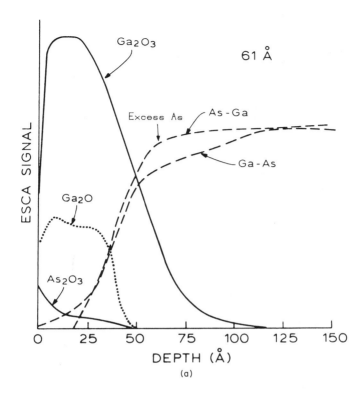

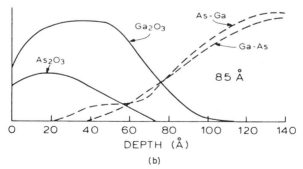

Figure 11. Chemical sputter depth profiles of (*a*) thermal and (*b*) anodic oxides on GaAs. (Reproduced from reference 64 with permission of the copyright owner.)

In the oxide, the ratio of Ga_2O_3 to As_2O_3 is 1 when corrected for differential sputtering effects.

Schwartz et al.[65] using ion milling to obtain chemical depth profiles of oxides on GaAs showed that As_2O_3 and Ga_2O_3 are not substantially reduced by the ion beam. Some differential sputtering of Ga relative to As occurs (Ga/As $\approx$ 1.3) on a cleaved (110) GaAs surface, and the $3d$ photoelectron peaks are broadened. As_2O_5 and $GaAsO_4$ powders were chemically modified by ion bombardment. These investigators' results for thermal oxides are similar to those of Wilmsen and co-workers.[66] Grunthaner and Maserjian[19] used NH_4OH/ethanol and argon (1 keV) to profile the native oxide on GaAs (see Figure 12). Ion damage is readily observed as smearing and broadening of the As $3d$ photoelectron peak. Chemical etching preserves the lineshapes. However, the Ga_2O_3 component of the film could not be removed entirely with this etchant. Some evidence is reported for the existence of $GaAsO_4$ on the surface of room temperature oxides. Kazmerski et al.[68] have studied wet and dry low temperature thermal oxides on polycrystalline CVD GaAs. Dry oxides are Ga_2O_3 and wet oxides are a mixture of Ga_2O_3, As_2O_3, and As_2O_5, demonstrating the significant role of water vapor in the formation of oxides on GaAs.

To summarize, the most studied III–V oxide is the oxide on GaAs since it has possible application to MOS device technology. Little attention has been paid to the actual width of the interface on this and other III–V interfaces because of their diffuse nature. At the time this chapter is being written, no systematic and detailed XPS study exists of oxide growth on GaAs as compared with the SiO_2/Si system. Published chemical depth profiles of the various oxides may require refinement due to the effects of differential sputtering, ion induced chemical reac-

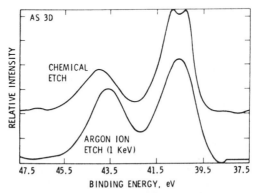

Figure 12. The effect of 1 keV Ar^+ on the thermal oxide (low temperature) of GaAs. (Reproduced from reference 19 with permission of the copyright owner.)

tions, ion reduction, etc. The work at Stanford using the SSRL facility has provided a good understanding of the basic chemistry of metal and oxygen interactions on ultraclean III–V surfaces.

6. SUMMARY

A number of very exciting applications of x-ray and synchrotron photoelectron spectroscopy to solid state device and device-like structures were reviewed. A number of methods have been employed in conjunction with XPS to provide chemical depth profiles of film structures on semiconductor substrates; the most common and perhaps the most "destructive" means is ion milling, or sputter etching. In the case of SiO_2 on Si and, to some extent, the oxide on GaAs system, ion milling causes chemical changes in the oxide and in the crucial interface region by ion-induced chemical reduction of the compound. This phenomenon is well known but not altogether characterized for many materials systems. F. J. Grunthaner has pioneered the use of controlled-volume chemical etch-back methods in a very successful attempt to eliminate or minimize damage to the SiO_2/Si interfacial region. Studies of oxides on GaAs were not so successful. Both methods remove film by chemical bond cleavage and produce surface damage which may appear as artifacts in the measurement, and this is unfortunately unavoidable. One can only hope to minimize damage and use a technique that provides technically significant information regarding the specific structure.[69]

In some cases, ion milling not only produces chemical reduction or modification but can also prove to be devastating when one is analyzing material systems in which cascade ion induced mixing is predominant. This phenomenon is well known from Rutherford backscattering studies. However, even in structures in which ion mixing is not probable, knock-on effects produce limited mixing and reordering over the ion range in the material. Therefore, it is very important to use the lowest possible ion energy to minimize this damage region or an ion that provides a small penetration depth relative to the information depth, especially in analyses that are aimed at the detailed chemistry of a thin interface layer.

The use of more sophisticated spectroscopic methods such as synchrotron radiation sources had allowed a number of investigators to study the surface of many materials during in situ film deposition or growth. The chemistry of the surface region within the information depth, which in the case of synchrotron radiation sources is tunable, is monitored as film deposition or growth proceeds.[61] This has resulted in a basic understanding of Schottky barrier formation on III–V compounds and provided a lead to the nature of the problems involved in MOS device fabrication.

Of the methods available for analysis, angle-resolved XPS, although limited to very-thin-film structures, can be as powerful as the synchrotron radiation source by providing a means of controlling the information depth. Ultraviolet spectroscopists have employed this technique with great success. However, only a few studies have been reported that use this method to characterize device interface properties. This technique is a most fruitful means of investigating device structures and is certainly more readily available than the synchrotron light sources.

XPS studies of SiO_2/Si, Pd/a-Si:H, Al/SiO_2/Si, SIPOS, Schottky barriers on III–V semiconductors, and thermal and anodic oxides on GaAs have been reviewed. These structures form a small sample of the present technology used in the electronics industry. In view of the vast XPS literature, it has not been possible here to review all the interesting studies. However, even the SiO_2/Si system should be further studied in a systematic fashion to determine the effect of various processes on the measurable interface chemistry; furthermore, these measurable quantities should be related to device electrical characteristics important to the industry.

REFERENCES

1. R. E. Honig and C. W. Magee, *Proceedings of the 26th Annual Conference on Mass Spectrometry and Allied Topics, St. Louis, Mo., 1978*, p. TB-4.

2. J. H. Thomas III, *IEEE Trans. Parts Hybrids Packaging*, **PHP-12**, 255 (1976).

3. K. Siegbahn et al., *ESCA Applied to Solids*, Almqvist & Wiksells, Uppsala, Sweden, 1967.

4. D. Briggs, in *Electron Spectroscopy: Theory, Techniques, and Applications* Vol. 3, C. R. Brundle and A. D. Baker, Eds., Academic Press, New York, 1979.

5. D. Briggs, *Handbook of X-ray and Ultraviolet Photoelectron Spectroscopy*, Heyden, London, 1977.

6. P. H. Holloway and G. E. McGuire, *Appl. Surface Sci.*, **4**, 410 (1980), and references therein.

7. T. C. McGill, *J. Vacuum Sci. Technol.*, **11**, 935 (1974).

8. A. Many, Y. Goldstein, and N. B. Grover, *Semiconductor Surfaces*, North-Holland Publs., Amsterdam, 1965.

9. M. L. Cohen, *J. Vacuum Sci. Technol.*, **16**, 1135 (1979).

10. S. Pantelides, Ed., *The Physics of SiO_2 and Its Interfaces*, Pergamon Press, Elmsford, N.Y., 1978.

11. K. S. Kim, W. E. Baitinger, J. W. Amy, and N. Winograd, *J. Electron Spectr.*, **5**, 351 (1974).

12. F. J. Grunthaner, P. J. Grunthaner, R. P. Vasquez, B. F. Lewis, J. Maserjian, and A. Madhukar, *J. Vacuum Sci. Technol.*, **16**, 1443 (1979).

13. S. Hofmann and J. H. Thomas III, *Surface Interface Anal.,* (1982), in press.
14. J. B. Bindell, J. W. Colby, D. R. Wonsidler, J. M. Poate, D. K. Conley, and T. C. Tisone, *Thin Solid Films,* **37**, 441 (1976).
15. Z. L. Liau, J. W. Mayer, W. L. Brown, and J. M. Poate, *J. Appl. Phys.,* **49**, 5295 (1978).
16. Z. L. Liau, B. Y. Tsaur, and J. W. Mayer, *J. Vacuum Sci. Technol.,* **16**, 121, (1979).
17. P. Williams and J. E. Baker, *Appl. Phys. Lett.,* **36**, 842 (1980).
18. U. Littmark and W. O. Hofer, *Nucl. Instrum. Methods,* **168**, 329 (1980), and references therein.
19. F. J. Grunthaner and J. Maserjian, in reference 10.
20. C. S. Fadley, *Progress Solid State Chem.,* **11**, 165 (1976).
21. C. S. Fadley, *J. Electron Spectr.,* **4**, 93 (1974).
22. D. E. Carlson and C. R. Wronski, *Appl. Phys. Lett.,* **28**, 671 (1976).
23. M. P. Seah and W. A. Dench, *Surface Int. Sci.,* **1**, 2 (1979).
24. C. J. Powell, in *Quantitative Surface Analysis of Materials,* N. S. McIntyre, Ed., American Society for Testing Materials, Philadelphia, 1978, ASTM STP-643.
25. R. Williams, *J. Vacuum Sci. Technol.,* **14**, 1106 (1977).
26. A. S. Grove, *Physics and Technology of Semiconductor Devices,* Wiley, New York, 1967, Chap. 12 (for example).
27. N. M. Johnson, D. J. Bartelink, and M. Schulz, in reference 10.
28. S. T. Pantelides and M. Long, in reference 10.
29. T. Hattori and T. Nishina, in reference 10.
30. J. H. Thomas III and G. W. Hughes, unpublished results (1978).
31. S. I. Raider and R. Flitsch, *IBM J. Res. Develop.,* **22**, 294 (1978).
32. S. I. Raider and R. Flitsch, *J. Electrochem. Soc.,* **123**, 1754 (1976).
33. S. I. Raider and R. Flitsch, *J. Vacuum Sci. Technol.,* **13**, 58 (1976).
34. R. A. Clarke, R. L. Tapping, M. A. Hopper, and L. Young, *J. Electrochem. Soc.,* **122**, 1347 (1975).
35. G. Hollinger, Y. Jugnet, P. Pertosa, L. Porte, and Tran Minh Duc, *Analysis* **5**, 2 (1977).
36. G. Hollinger, Y. Jugnet, P. Pertosa, L. Porte, and Tran Minh Duc, *Proceedings of the 7th International Vacuum Congress and the 3rd International Conference on Solid Surfaces, Vienna, 1977,* p. 2229.
37. G. Hollinger, Y. Jugnet, P. Pertosa, and Tran Minh Duc, *Chem. Phys. Lett.,* **36**, 441 (1975).
38. S. Iwata and A. Ishizaka, *J. Japan Inst. Metals,* **43**, 380 (1979).
39. A. Ishizaka, S. Iwata, and Y. Kamigaki, *Surface Sci.,* **84**, 355 (1979).
40. A. Ishizaka and S. Iwata, *Appl. Phys. Lett.,* **36**, 71 (1980).

41. J. M. Hill, D. G. Royce, C. S. Fadley, L. F. Wagner, and F. J. Grunthaner, *Chem. Phys. Lett.*, **44**, 225 (1976).

42. R. S. Bauer, J. C. McMenamin, H. Petersen, and A. Bianconi, in reference 10.

43. A. M. Goodman, *Phys. Rev.*, **152**, 780 (1966); **152**, 785 (1966).

44. F. J. Grunthaner, P. J. Grunthaner, R. P. Vasanez, B. F. Lewis, and J. Maserjian, *Phys. Rev. Lett.*, **43**, 1683 (1979).

45. W. L. Harrington, R. E. Honig, A. M. Goodman, and R. Williams, *Appl. Phys. Lett.*, **27**, 644 (1975).

46. L. C. Feldman, in reference 10.

47. C. R. Helms, W. E. Spicer, and N. M. Johnson, *Solid State Commun.*, **25**, 673 (1978).

48. R. Z. Bachrach and R. S. Bauer, *J. Vacuum Sci. Technol.*, **16**, 1149 (1979).

49. J. H. Thomas III and D. E. Carlson, *J. Electrochem. Soc.*, **128**, 415 (1981).

50. D. E. Carlson, C. W. Magee, and J. H. Thomas III, *Solar Cells,* **1**, 371 (1980).

51. M. Hamasaki, T. Adachi, S. Wakayama, and M. Kikuchi, *J. Appl. Phys.*, **49**, 3987 (1980).

52. J. H. Thomas III and A. M. Goodman, *J. Electrochem. Soc.*, **126**, 1766 (1979).

53. T. Adachi and C. R. Helms, *J. Electrochem. Soc.*, **127**, (1980).

54. H. H. Wieder, *J. Vacuum Sci. Technol.*, **15**, 1498 (1978); **17**, 1009 (1980).

55. P. Pianetta, I. Lindau, C. Garner, and W. E. Spicer, *Phys. Rev. Lett.*, **35**, 1356 (1975).

56. I. Lindau, P. W. Chye, C. M. Garner, P. Pianetta, C. Y. Su, and W. E. Spicer, *J. Vacuum Sci. Technol.*, **15**, 1332 (1978).

57. P. W. Chye, C. Y. Su, I. Lindau, P. Skeath, and W. E. Spicer, *J. Vacuum Sci. Technol.*, **16**, 1191 (1979).

58. P. Skeath, I. Lindau, P. W. Chye, C. Y. Su, and W. E. Spicer, *J. Vacuum Sci. Technol.*, **16**, 1143 (1979).

59. W. E. Spicer, P. W. Chye, P. Skeath, C. Y. Su, and I. Lindau, *J. Vacuum Sci. Technol.*, **16**, 1422 (1979).

60. L. J. Brillson, *J. Vacuum Sci. Technol.*, **16**, 1137 (1979).

61. R. W. Grant, J. R. Waldrop, and E. A. Kraut, *J. Vacuum Sci. Technol.*, **15**, 1451 (1978).

62. P. Pianetta, I. Lindau, and W. E. Spicer, *Quantitative Surface Analysis of Materials,* N. S. McIntyre, Ed., American Society for Testing Materials, Philadelphia, 1978, ASTM STP-643.

63. W. E. Spicer, in *Electron and Ion Spectroscopy of Solids,* L. Fiermans, J. Vennik, and W. Dekeyser, Eds., Plenum, New York, 1978.

64. Y. Mizokawa, H. Iwasaki, R. Nishitani, and S. Nakamura, *J. Electron Spectr.*, **14**, 129 (1978).

65. G. P. Schwartz, G. J. Gualtien, G. W. Kammlott, and B. Schwartz, *J. Electrochem. Soc.,* **126**, 1737 (1979).

66. C. W. Wilmsen, R. W. Kee, and K. M. Geib, *J. Vacuum Sci. Technol.,* **16**, 1434 (1979), and references therein.

67. K. M. Geib and C. W. Wilmsen, *J. Vacuum Sci. Technol.,* **17**, 952 (1980).

68. L. L. Kazmerski, P. J. Ireland, S. S. Chu, and Y. T. Lee, *J. Vacuum Sci. Technol.,* **17**, 521 (1980).

69. G. E. McGuire, *Surface Sci.,* **76**, 130 (1978).

CHAPTER

4

X-RAY PHOTOELECTRON SPECTROSCOPY APPLICATIONS IN PHOTOVOLTAICS RESEARCH

L. L. KAZMERSKI

Photovoltaic Device and Measurements Branch
Solar Energy Research Institute
Golden, Colorado

1. INTRODUCTION

The performance, cost, and reliability of a photovoltaic system depends both primarily and ultimately on its basic building component—the solar cell. However, these three ingredients—performance, cost, reliability—seem interrelated in such a way that a gain in one adversely affects one or both of the others. For example, the cost of photovoltaic devices can be significantly reduced by using polycrystalline thin films to fabricate the device instead of single crystals. However, this less perfect material limits the solar conversion efficiency and can constrain device lifetime due to enhanced degradation mechanisms at crystalline defects. Therefore, the major portion of photovoltaic research and development activity is concerned with balancing these three aspects to bring about economic feasibility for this technology.[1] At present, no device technology completely satisfies these requirements, nor does any device type present a clear and universal choice for terrestrial photovoltaics.

Photovoltaic device performance depends (as do other semiconductor technologies) upon the *composition* of the constituent materials and the stability of the numerous *interfaces* between and within the various structural layers. Because of these basic considerations, it is evident that surface analysis and microanalysis is required to understand and improve device performance and to uncover the physicochemical mechanisms that cause the device degradation. Unless adequate performance is attained over reasonable lifetimes (e.g., 10 to 20 years), photovoltaics cannot be expected to compete with current technologies for the large residential and, eventually, utility markets.[2]

The number of surface analysis methods useful to the investigation of surface and interface problems in photovoltaic research is extensive.[3] The strengths and limitations of each of these techniques are best evaluated with respect to the application and the information required. Three methods which are most frequently used are Auger-electron spectroscopy (AES), secondary-ion mass spectroscopy (SIMS), and x-ray photoelectron spectroscopy (XPS). Each has a different input probe (electrons, ions, and x-rays, respectively), and the information gained by each can complement that obtained by the others. AES provides excellent spatial resolution, with probe diameters currently in the sub-500-Å range. With scanning capabilities, impurity mapping can be obtained. It is limited in elemental sensitivity ($\sim$0.1 atomic %) and cannot detect hydrogen, which is important to semiconductor properties. SIMS, on the other hand, can detect hydrogen and has at least 100 times the sensitivity of AES. However, spatial resolution is not as good. XPS suffers in this respect also, but information on composition, and especially chemical bonding, is obtainable with a minimum of probe-induced damage or artifacts. In this chapter, the usefulness of XPS in photovoltaic device investigations is highlighted and overviewed. Emphasis is placed upon the chemical phase identification and analysis at multielemental solar cell interfaces, including oxide/semiconductor, metal/semiconductor, semiconductor/semiconductor, and internal grain boundaries. Examples of single crystal and polycrystalline Si, GaAs, InP, and Zn_3P_2 solar cells are presented. Results of the compositional analyses are correlated with device performance parameters and with specific areal electrical activity using in situ electron-beam induced current (EBIC) methods. The importance and benefits of combining the XPS results with other surface analysis techniques for the unambiguous solution of some device interface problems are discussed.

2. TECHNIQUES

The theory and general operational aspects of XPS have been covered in detail in several previous publications,[4-9] as well as in this volume. The purpose of this chapter is to stress the usefulness and applications of x-ray photoelectron spectroscopy (XPS) to problem solution in photovoltaic research and development (R&D). Throughout, the capacity of XPS to provide composition and chemical bonding information in a minimally disruptive manner is emphasized. However, no *single* technique can be expected to universally yield unambiguous solutions to the wide range of compositional and chemical problems encountered in such device research.[1] Thus, the complementary use of surface analysis techniques underlies the investigations reviewed here. In order to better interpret results and to minimize the generation of experimental artifacts that could provide incorrect conclusions, an understanding of the strengths and limitations of each investigative tool must be gained. All of these have been reviewed in the literature[10-13] and will not be reexamined here. Table 1 provides some general comparisons of several features important to the surface analysis tools considered in the following section. Evaluations of this sort can assist the surface analyst in choosing and combining techniques in order to maximize the information obtained from the analysis. However, it is the combination of available information from the literature with the researcher's operational knowledge and experience with the materials and techniques that provides the best basis for dependable surface analysis results.

Commercial instrumentation has been used in the applications presented herein. A Physical Electronics Industries Model 550 XPS/SAM system was used primarily. The ion gun used for SIMS and depth profiling was differentially pumped, with a 100-μm minimum ion-beam diameter, measured at full width at half-maximum height (FWHM). Argon was used as the sputtering gas. This source was capable of being rastered over a maximum 1 cm $\times$ 1 cm area, with typically less than an order of magnitude rise in background pressure during ion etching. The SIMS system used an Extranuclear Laboratories quadrupole mass anlayzer (QMA). This system was capable of examining mass species over the 1–1000 amu range. The scanning AES had a minimum spot size of 3.4 μm, and utilized a double-pass cylindrical mirror analyzer. The analyses were performed in an ultrahigh-vacuum environment, with a base pressure of 1.5 $\times$ 10^{-10} torr. For the XPS studies, a Mg$K\alpha$ x-ray source was operated at 10 kV. The double-pass analyzer was equipped for angular-resolved photoemission experiments. For most applications a 15-eV pass energy was used, and a 10-eV pass energy was employed for the angular resolved studies. The analysis area by XPS was approximately 1.5 mm^2. All three analysis techniques could be performed simultaneously on the same sample area.

3. APPLICATIONS

Photovoltaic devices present both a variety and a number of interfaces that are critical to device performance.[14] For thin-film technologies, these interfaces become even more important since changes in the interfacial regions (e.g., via interdiffusion, impurity segregation, solid-state reactions, etc.) are more likely to

TABLE 1. Basic Comparisons of Auger Electron Spectroscopy, Secondary Ion Mass Spectroscopy, and X-ray Photoelectron Spectroscopy

Specification	AES	SIMS	XPS
Excitation	Electrons	Ions	X-rays
Emission	Electrons	+, −Ions	Electrons
Analysis area, minimum (μm)	$\sim10^{-1}$ to 10^{-2}	$\sim10^{0}$	$\sim10^{3}$
Analysis depth (μm)	10^{-3}	5×10^{-4}	10^{-3}
Distructiveness	Low to medium	High	Very low
Depth information	With sputtering	Direct	With sputtering
Quantification	Easy (0.1–1.0% with standards)	Difficult	Most reliable
Sensitivity (atomic %)	0.1	~0.001	0.1
Mapping	High resolution	Medium resolution	Low resolution
Relative interpretation	Easy	Medium to difficult	Medium
Chemical information	Yes—with experience	Molecular species	Yes

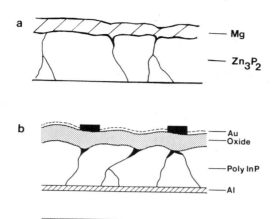

Figure 1. Schematic cross-sectional representations of polycrystalline photovoltaic devices: (a) Mg/Zn$_3$P$_2$ Schottky barrier; (b) Au/oxide/InP MIS device.

affect the relatively thin layers they separate. In polycrystalline solar cells, such interactions can become very pronounced at the intergrain or grain boundary regions.[15] Thus, while conceptually the solar cell is a large-area electronic device, the mechanisms occurring at the microscopic scale are often those which dominate or determine the macroscopic operation. It is in these areas that XPS and other, higher-resolution surface analysis techniques have demonstrated their exceptional diagnostic capabilities. Figure 1 shows schematically the cross sections of two typical photovoltaic device structures, the metal–semiconductor [or Schottky barrier (Figure 1a)], and the metal–insulator–semiconductor [or MIS (Figure 1b)] solar cell. Each provides several material interfaces, complicated by grain boundary intersections. It is the integrity of these interfaces that is critical to maintaining device performance and reliability. And it is these interfaces that are most sensitive to the operating conditions (illumination, temperature gradients, electrical fields, etc.) and even to the rather severe processing that the devices endure during their fabrication.

This section illustrates the importance of XPS and other surface analysis methods to uncovering such problems, to minimizing their effects, and to understanding the physical, compositional, and chemical processes that dominate the operation of these devices. Four examples are presented that partially represent the diversity of applications that surface analysis methods can serve in photovoltaic research. The first two deal with two different metal–semiconductor junction (Schottky barrier) device problems. In the presumed Mg/Zn$_2$P$_2$ photovoltaic device, XPS identifies a reaction between the metal and the semiconductor, which leads to the formation of a heterojunction—rather than a Schottky barrier—solar cell. In the Au/polycrystalline GaAs device, XPS, AES and SIMS provide physical evidence for both reduced open-circuit voltage and the operational instability. Third, chemical and compositional problems associated with oxide quality and oxide/semiconductor interfaces are presented for InP MIS solar cells. Finally, angular-resolved XPS is utilized to evaluate a grain boundary passivation scheme for polycrystalline Si devices.

3.1. Zn_3P_2 Solar Cell

Zn_2P_2 is a promising semiconductor for photovoltaic device application because of its nearly optimum electronic and optical properties,[16-19] and the abundance of the constituent elements.[20] Only p-type Zn_3P_2 has been reported for device fabrication, limiting its application to other than homojunctions. The best devices have used Mg to form a Schottky barrier[16] as shown in Figure 1a. Good quality polycrystalline Zn_3P_2 thin films have been produced by closed-space vapor transport.[16] Controlled n-type doping is obtained by using Ag. A typical XPS spectrum of a Ag-doped Zn_3P_2 film is presented in Figure 2. The expected Zn and P lines are evident, with the 0- to –200-eV binding energy range expanded in the insert. The Ag dopant (p ~ $10^{19}/cm^3$) is seen by the presence of the Ag $3d_{5/2}$ and $3d_{3/2}$ lines. The chemical shift in the Zn $2p_{3/2}$ line is 0.9 eV from the elemental Zn position.

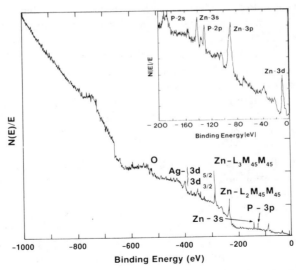

Figure 2. XPS survey spectra of Ag-doped Zn_3P_2. Insert presents expanded spectrum for 0 to –200-eV binding energy range, showing Zn 3s, 3p, and 3d lines, and P 2s and 2p lines.

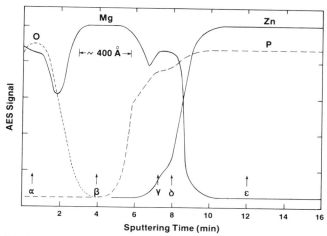

Figure 3. AES depth-compositional profile of Mg/Zn$_3$P$_2$ solar cell. Reaction between the Mg and Zn$_3$P$_2$ is indicated at γ. (From Kazmerski et al.[22])

The device operational characteristics resulting from the Mg/Zn$_3$P$_2$ fabrication have not been consistent with the formation of a Schottky barrier solar cell. For example, anomalies in barrier heights and in spectral response have been observed.[16,21] Some of these differences have been explained by analyzing the Mg/Zn$_3$P$_2$ interface using depth profiling and XPS.[22] The interaction of the Mg with the Zn$_3$P$_2$ layer is indicated in the AES depth-compositional profile of Figure 3. Some oxide at the Mg surface is in evidence, resulting from heat treatment in air (100°C, 2 hr) following device fabrication. The approximately 400-Å-thick Mg layer is relatively clean, but the interface with the Zn$_3$P$_2$ is somewhat complex. The response of the AES Mg signal and the shoulder in the P signal suggest an interaction between these species. In order to ascertain the chemical properties of the various layers and interfaces, XPS was used in conjunction with these depth-profile results.

A series of XPS spectra (over the binding energy range –96 to –84 eV) is presented in Figure 4 for the points α through ϵ in Figure 3. The surface oxide at α is identified to be primarily MgO from the position of the 2s line, shifted 1.2 eV from the Mg 2s line at point β.[23] At γ, where the apparent reaction between the Mg and Zn$_3$P$_2$ occurs, an additional shift in the 2s line is measured. This peak could not be identified from available literature data. The formation of some Mg–P compound was speculated from the results of the apparent relationship between the Mg and P AES signals at this interface. A polycrystalline Mg$_3$P$_2$ standard was prepared by direct reactive combination of the elements in vacuo, and its structure was verified by x-ray diffraction. The shift in the Mg 2s peak at γ corresponds directly to the 2s Mg$_3$P$_2$ peak of the standard

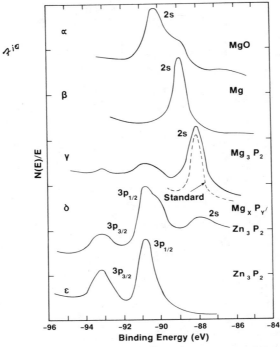

Figure 4. XPS spectra for point α through ϵ of Figure 3. Dashed line represents data for Mg_3P_2 standard sample. (From Kazmerski et al.[22])

(dashed peak in Figure 4). The presence of this compound at the interface changes the nature of the photovoltaic device significantly. At δ, some remnant of this $2s$ peak is observable, in addition to the $Zn(Zn_3P_2)$ $3p_{1/2}$ and $3p_{3/2}$ lines. Finally, these two lines dominate at ϵ, the interior of the Zn_3P_2.

These XPS studies have identified the presence of Mg_3P_2 at the reacted Mg/Zn_3P_2 interface. Mg_3P_2 is a semiconductor with approximately a 1.6 eV bandgap. Thus, the XPS results confirm the formation of a *heterojunction* (rather than a Schottky barrier) after higher-doped ($p > 10^{17}/cm^3$) Zn_3P_2 is annealed for short periods (1–2 hr) in contact with the Mg. Recently, Catalano and Bhushan[21] have reported that a buried homojunction can form if longer ($\sim$24 hr) annealing times are used and the Zn_3P_2 has a lower carrier concentration ($p < 10^{16}/cm^3$). However, the application of XPS to this interface problem explains the initial electrical and optical behavior of Mg/Zn_3P_2 thin-film solar cells. Although the AES data suggested the interaction, the XPS measurement provided the chemical identification.

3.2. GaAs Schottky Barrier

Au has been a common metallization for the fabrication of GaAs Schottky barrier and MIS solar cells.[24-29] However, some significant variations in barrier heights have been reported, which seem to depend critically upon the metal deposition conditions, especially substrate temperature.[25,30,31] Even for Au/GaAs devices produced at room temperatures, there have been indications that the model of a simple, abrupt metal–semiconductor junction is not adequate for explaining electrical behavior.[25,31-34] Although some of these departures from the expected behavior can be accounted for by interfacial oxides or impurities, the evidence also exists for devices produced in vacuo, after vacuum cleaving.[35] These observations indicate the possibility of interfacial chemical activity between the Au and the GaAs.

Studies similar to those outlined for the Zn_3P_2 device have been performed. Figure 5 presents a SIMS depth profile of a device composed of a 200-Å Au layer on a MBE-grown, polycrystalline GaAs film (Sn-doped, $N_D \sim 10^{16}/cm^3$, 10 μm thick).[36] Static SIMS has better surface sensitivity than AES or XPS, and it can sometimes be used to pronouncedly show the region of interaction at such interfaces. (The reason of this difference in surface sensitivity is due to the larger escape depths of Auger or photoejected electrons compared to the removal of single atomic layers in SIMS.) In Figure 5, plateaus in the ^{197}Au and ^{69}Ga signals are observable at the interface of this room-temperature-produced device. The XPS Au $4f_{7/2}$ signal was measured across this interface; these data are compared in Figure 6 for the top Au layer (the reference), and the points α and β indicated on Figure 5. The XPS signal from the Au film itself yields the expected spectrum, with the $4f_{7/2}$ peak at 83.8 eV and the $4f_{5/2}$ at 87.3 eV. At point α of Figure 5, a double peak is observed—the elemental Au 83.8 eV peak, and another near 85 eV. This second one has been ascribed to a chemical shift due to the chemical reaction of the Au and Ga. This reaction is further confirmed by the XPS data taken at point β. Here, only *one* peak is evident, shifted to 85.1 eV from the elemental Au position. This chemical shift corresponds to Ga_2Au,[37] and the formation of this phase has been previously demonstrated at higher temperatures. These data (Figures 5 and 6) were the first direct physical evidence for the reaction of Au with GaAs at lower temperatures.[37]

The degradation effects of the Au–Ga reaction has been correlated with the electrical properties of this junction. Table 2 presents the variation in Schottky barrier height as a function of annealing. After room-temperature deposition, the barrier heights are 0.89 ± 0.04 eV. These barrier heights were obtained from the temperature dependence of the forward-biased current–voltage characteristics, and are within 1 eV of other reported values.[24,25,32,35,38,39] This "usual" value is below the expected 1.0 eV value.[38] As the device is heated, severe

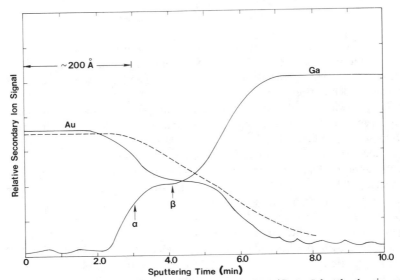

Figure 5. Positive SIMS depth-compositional profile of Au/GaAs Schottky barrier solar cell. [197]Au and [69]Ga mass peaks are monitored for as-deposited (solid lines) and annealed (450°C, 20 min) devices (broken line); α and β indicate points at which XPS data were taken. (From Kazmerski and Ireland.[36])

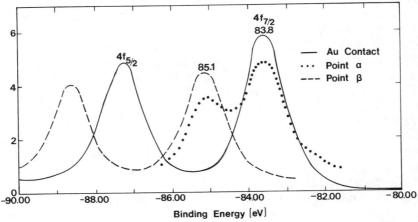

Figure 6. XPS spectra, showing Au peaks and chemical shifts for Au contact, point α in Figure 5, and point β in Figure 5. (From Kazmerski and Ireland.[36])

70

TABLE 2. Summary of Schottky Barrier Height Variations as a Function of Temperature (20-min Anneals) for Au/GaAs Devices

$T(^\circ C)$	27	100	200	250	325	400	450
$q\phi_b$(eV)	0.89	0.87	0.79	0.71	0.67	0.64	0.55

interdiffusion occurs—with both the width of the Ga_2Au region increasing (determined by XPS and AES depth profiles) and penetration of the GaAs by the Au taking place (see the dashed line in Figure 5). In Polycrystalline GaAs, the diffusion is greatly enhanced at the grain boundaries and the diffusion coefficients have been reported.[36] At temperatures above 350°C the barrier heights have degraded by about 25%, in an irreversible manner.[36]

Thus, XPS has been used in conjunction with SIMS depth profiling to identify both the chemical reaction between Au and GaAs and the reacted species itself, Ga_2Au. This phase accounts for the lower than expected barrier height and the instability of the Au/GaAs Schottky barrier at elevated temperatures.

3.3. InP MIS Device

Currently, solar cells using insulator–semiconductor interfaces comprise a significant portion of photovoltaic R & D activity.[1,40] The inclusion of an oxide—usually 10–50 Å thick—between the metal and semiconductor *ideally* isolates the grain boundaries in polycrystalline thin films, provides high open-circuit voltages and retains (for proper oxide thickness) respectable short-circuit current densities. A cross section of the device used as the present example is shown in Figure 1b.[41] The InP was grown by CVD, and was S-doped, 20–30 μm in thickness, with $n \sim 10^{17}$/cm^3. Two methods of oxidation were utilized in this study of low-temperature (i.e., less energy intensive processing and lower cost) methods of device production. The *dry process* involves the in situ oxidation of the InP immediately following film growth, in O_2 gas at 200°C for 1–2 hr. The *wet process* is done at about 100°C by passing oxygen saturated in water vapor over the samples, which were etched in HCl prior to oxide growth. The oxidation time was 24 hr in this case to provide the same 100-Å-thick film as the dry case. A 100–200 Å Au layer was vacuum deposited to complete the device.

Figure 7 presents a depth-compositional profile of the dry oxide/InP interface. The solid lines represent the AES data (O_{KLL}, In_{MNN}, and P_{LMM} transitions); the dashed lines, the SIMS data. By either method, a relatively uniform oxide layer and orderly transition from the oxide to the InP are observed. Some minor accumulation of the S-dopant at the interface region is apparent in the SIMS profile. In addition, a low sulfur concentration seems to penetrate the oxide

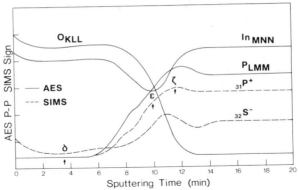

Figure 7. Depth-compositional profile of dry oxide/polycrystalline InP interface using AES and SIMS. (From Kazmerski et al.[41])

layer to the oxide surface. No sulfur was detected by AES. Some accumulation of the InP dopant was detected at the semiconductor surface of nonoxidized films, possibly at the grain boundaries. It is presumed that this surface S accumulation is the source of the SIMS $^{32}S^-$ signal observed at the oxide/InP interface and is not due to impurity segregation during growth.

For comparison, a depth profile of a wet oxide/polycrystalline InP interface is shown in Figure 8. These data are taken under the identical conditions as those of Figure 7. In this case, the oxide layer can be seen to be quite nonuniform and the transition region is more complex. The SIMS data are taken on two distinctly different locations on the sample. The $^{32}S^-$ and $^{31}P^+$ profiles taken over a rather large-grain region show far less penetration into the oxide than does the profile over a grain boundary intersection. In addition, the accumulation of $^{35}Cl^-$ is observed in the profile in Figure 8.

In order to better compare the chemical composition of the wet and dry oxides, XPS data were obtained at various points during the depth profiles of Figure 7 and 8. The position of the In $3d_{3/2}$ and $3d_{5/2}$ peaks in the XPS spectrum of the dry oxide (taken at point δ in Figure 7) are presented in Figure 9a. These peaks (referenced to the $4f_{7/2}$ and $4f_{5/2}$ peaks from an Au standard and the $3d_{5/2}$ and $3d_{3/2}$ peaks from an In standard) are shifted by 1.0 and 1.3 eV, respectively, from their pure In positions and correspond to In_2O_3.[42] No other signals were observed over this binding-energy range. In contrast, Figure 9b presents XPS data, taken under identical conditions to those in Figure 9a, for the wet oxide at point β in Figure 8. This spectrum is more structured, with several additional peaks corresponding to various other chemical species. To identify these, XPS spectra were taken for a number of stable In-based compounds, using high-purity standards. These data are shown in Table 2. The major peaks in

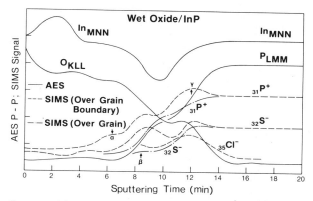

Figure 8. Depth-compositional profile of wet oxide/polycrystalline InP interface using AES and SIMS. SIMS data over grain-region and grain-boundary intersection are shown. (From Kazmerski et al.[41])

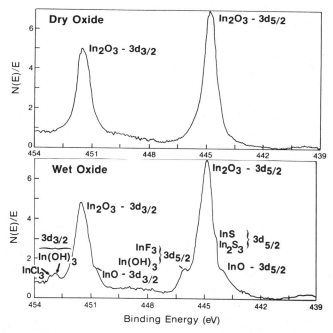

Figure 9. XPS spectra of wet and dry oxides on InP. Dry oxide data taken at point δ in Figure 7; wet oxide, at point β in Figure 8.

73

TABLE 3. Summary of XPS and Auger Peak Energy Positions for Various In Species Determined Experimentally Using Standard Specimens[a]

In species	$3d_{5/2}$ (eV)	$3d_{3/2}$ (eV)	Δ (eV)[b]	$M_4N_{45}N_{45}$ (eV)	$M_5N_{45}N_{45}$ (eV)
In	443.6	451.2	7.6	843.1	851.0
InP	444.0	451.6	7.6	842.6	850.4
In_2S_3 (InS)	444.4	452.4	8.0	841.5	849.9
In_2O_3	444.9	452.2	7.3	839.8	847.1
In_2O	444.0	450.9	6.9	839.2	846.4
$InCl_3$	445.8	453.2	7.4	836.4	844.4
In (OH)$_3$	445.8	452.9	7.1	837.4	844.5

[a]From Kazmerski et al.[35].
[b]Here, Δ is the energy difference between the In $3d_{5/2}$ and In $3d_{3/2}$ peaks.

Figure 9b correspond (as for the dry oxide) to the $3d_{3/2}$ and $3d_{5/2}$ In (In_2O_3) signals. The peaks at 444.0 and 450.9 eV correspond both in position and peak energy separation (Δ) to In_2O.[43] Due to the S accumulation near the interface (indicated by the SIMS data in Figure 8), the presence of sulfur/indium species was expected. The XPS peak at 444.4 eV corresponds to the In_2S_3 (or InS) $3d_{5/2}$ peak. The $3d_{3/2}$ peak is presumably masked by the $3d_{3/2}$ In_2O_3 peak at 452.2 eV. The remaining peaks [$InCl_3$ and In(OH)$_3$] are due to the surface treatment (HCl etch) of the InP layer prior to oxidation. In almost all cases, the compounds were verified by the positions of the Auger $M_4N_{45}N_{45}$ and $M_5N_{45}N_{45}$ peaks generated in the XPS spectra. These Auger transitions are also summarized in Table 3. The only problem was distinguishing between the In_2S_3 and InS phases. Standard samples from each of these generated identical XPS spectra. It is presumed, however, that In_2S_3 is the compound detected since it is more easily formed.[41] Finally, the XPS data in Figures 7 and 8 and those listed in Table 3 were compared to the literature data and found to be in agreement for In,[42] InS,[45] In_2O_3,[42] In_2O,[43] and $InCl_3$.[43]

SIMS has been used previously to determine the impurity content of these oxides.[41] In general, the dry oxides are relatively clean. In contrast, the SIMS spectra of the wet oxides indicate the presence of several of the molecular species detected by XPS, including In_2O^+, $InCl_3^+$, InS^+, and $In(OH)_3^+$. The accumulation of several impurities (S^+, Cl^-, P^+, Ch_x^+, Mg^+, Si^+, Ca^+) at the wet oxide/InP interface have also been detected. This accumulation is later identified by EBIC as one source of current loss in the solar cell. Further evidence of P accumulation at the interface is gained from the XPS data of Figure 10. Near the interface for each oxide type (at point ζ in Figure 7 and point γ in Figure 8) an

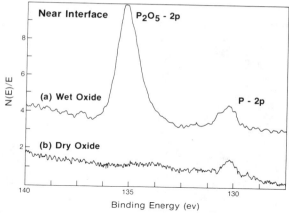

Figure 10. XPS spectra of oxides, near oxide/InP interface: (*a*) wet oxide at point γ in Figure 8; (*b*) dry oxide at point ζ in Figure 7. Presence of elemental phosphorus is indicated. (From Kazmerski et al.[41])

elemental P signal is observed in the XPS spectrum of Figure 10. The P signal occurs at a 130.1-eV binding energy, shifted 2.5 eV from the position of the P 2*p* peak in InP, indicating excess P. These observations are in agreement with those reported by Wilmsen and Kee.[46] The spectra also differ at these two points in that P_2O_5 is observed in the wet oxide. An examination of the depth profile of Figure 8 in the region of γ shows a plateau in the oxygen signal. At point ζ in Figure 7 the oxygen KLL signal has almost reached its minimum point.

Figure 11 presents EBIC scans of the dry and wet oxides. Figures 11*b*1 and 11*b*2 show intensity and line modulation EBIC responses of the dry oxides. Although the response is somewhat nonuniform, no regions of excessive current loss are observable. In comparison, Figures 11*a*1 and 11*b*1 show similar data for the wet oxide case. Obvious current loss is observed along positions corresponding to grain boundaries. It has been proposed that based upon the EBIC, XPS, and SIMS evidence, the grain boundaries are sites for impurity accumulation and resultant current loss in these devices.[41] The impurity accumulation is dependent upon the method of oxidation.

Solar cells fabricated from these MIS structures have demonstrated marginal performance to date, with efficiencies 2–4% under AM1 conditions.[41] Devices using the dry oxides have shown more consistent results over larger areas than those using the wet oxides. This is presumably due to the more uniform electrical activity of the dry oxide based device. Obviously, more research must be done on optimizing the oxide/InP interface as well as the oxide layer itself before

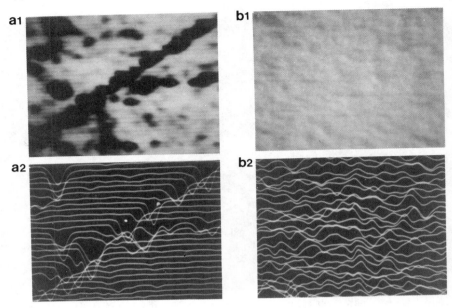

Figure 11. EBIC scans of oxide layers: (a1) Intensity-modulated EBIC, wet oxide; (a2) line-modulated EBIC, same area as a1; (b1) intensity-modulated EBIC, dry oxide; (b2) line-modulated EBIC, same area as b1. (From Kazmerski et al.[41])

worthwhile polycrystalline solar cells of this type are demonstrated, although these surface analysis studies have provided some identification of the source of the performance limitations.

3.4. Si Grain Boundary Passivation

Polycrystalline Si is considered a major candidate for photovoltaic device applications, primarily due to its potential lower cost, efficient material utilization, and material abundance and availability. One limiting factor to adequate device performance remains the problem of carrier loss via recombination and/or shunting at grain boundaries.[47] Currently, a large effort is aimed at passivating or isolating these regions using various chemical methods.[45-50] Among these, the most prevalent methods involve the incorporation of impurities, namely, H, Li, F, O, along the boundary to presumably satisfy dangling bonds (to minimize recombination) or to chemically react with conducting species (to minimize shunting).

One potential passivation scheme utilizes the nonuniform oxidation of polycrystalline Si.[51] The initial oxidation of Si and the Si/SiO_2 interface has been

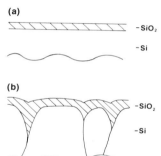

Figure 12. Schematic representation of oxidation of (a) single-grain region and (b) grain-boundary (polycrystalline) region.

the subject of many studies.[52-69] In this passivation process, the grain boundary penetration of the oxide during the initial oxidation period is utilized. This difference is illustrated in Figure 12. For a single-grain region (Figure 12a), the oxide grows uniformly. However, for a region containing grain boundaries, the oxidation seems to nucleate first at these regions, providing thicker oxides over the grain boundaries. Thus, by either stopping the oxidation process early or by uniformly etching the oxide after growth over the entire sample, the passivating oxide could be controlled over the grain boundaries only, leaving the grains exposed for further processing.[51]

Angular-resolved XPS[70,71] studies have been performed in order to better resolve the differences in oxidation between the intragrain and intergrain regions[51] Figures 13a and 13b present XPS data for a Si sample that has been oxidized at 220°C for 24 min. These data have been processed using a standard mathematical deconvolution routine.[72,73] Here, θ is defined as the angle between the sample normal and the effective analyzer entrance or acceptance area. At lower values of θ, electrons from deeper into sample appear in the spectrum. As θ increases, electrons are analyzed from nearer the sample surface, with the result that the data taken at higher θ values are more surface sensitive.[54] All data were taken with the Si $2p$ signal at approximately 6×10^3 cps.

The polycrystalline Si used in these investigations was produced by casting, using high-purity semiconductor grade poly-Si as the source material. Samples were selected to provide both large (7-10 mm) and small (0.1-0.5 mm) grain sizes. The surface of the grains was typically a ⟨001⟩ orientation. The samples were finely polished (0.01 μm final finish) and cleaned with a NaOH etch immediately before insertion into the vacuum chamber. Prior to oxidation, the polished Si surface was cleaned using Ar ion etching, while monitoring the oxygen and carbon Auger peaks as an indication of surface readiness. Typical etching time was 10 sec, and no oxygen was detected at either grain or grain boundary regions. Examination at 8k magnification showed no resulting surface

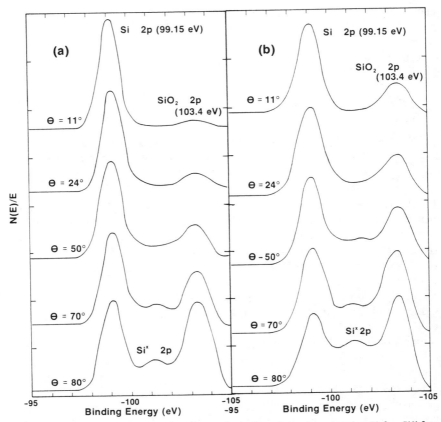

Figure 13. Angular-resolved XPS spectra of (*a*) single-grain region, showing Si 2*p*, Si^*x*^ 2*p*, and SiO₂ 2*p* peaks as a function of θ; (*b*) grain-boundary region, under same conditions as for part *a*. (From Kazmerski et al.[51])

texturing. Changes in the surface characteristics were detected only after sputtering for more than 45 sec under these conditions. Etching parameters were 5 kV, I_p = 2μA, with a 0.9 × 0.9 cm raster area, using a differentially pumped ion gun. The sample could be heated in the analysis chamber to 350°C for oxide growth, although data to 220°C are presented in this study. For oxidation, research-grade oxygen was directed at the sample surface using a stainless-steel capillary located 5 cm from the sample and controlled by a leak valve. The ultrahigh-vacuum chamber had a 1 × 10⁻¹⁰ torr background pressure, and the pressure during oxidation typically ranged from 8 × 10⁻⁸ to 2 × 10⁻⁷ torr. A quadrupole mass analyzer was used to monitor the background species during the oxidation process in order to ensure that oxygen was the only gas species introduced into the chamber. The ion gauge was left off during the oxidation. The time required to bring the oxygen to the desired level was 10 sec, much less than the total oxidation processing times, which usually exceeded 10 min. The oxygen leak rate in steady state was 10^{-9} torr-liters/sec, determined from a calibration of the leak valve. The exact dose rate was not measured for this system, but is approximately 10^{13} molecules/cm^2 based upon the leak rate and the 1-cm^2 surface area. (This magnitude is consistent with the dose rates evaluated by Madey for a precision gas-dosing system.[75]) During oxidation, the electron beam was *not* on in order to prevent electron-beam–induced oxidation.

Figure 13a represents XPS data measured on a flat single-grain region having a 4-mm diameter. At $\theta = 11°$, a large Si 2p signal is observed at –99.15 eV,[76] with a much smaller SiO$_2$ 2p signal at –103.4 eV.[76] As θ increases, the SiO$_2$ 2p line becomes more pronounced since more of the signal comes from the oxide layer itself. An additional peak at –101.1 eV becomes observable at higher θ, and this 2p peak is associated with the Si^x interfacial layer.[77,78] The composition and width of this interfacial layer is still a subject of much discussion, although some oxide is presumed.[77-79]

Figure 13b presents similar data taken under identical conditions as those in Figure 13a but on a region with a high population of grain boundaries (i.e., a region of small grain size). AES depth profiles, using a high-resolution (1500-Å beam diameter scanning Auger microscopy (SAM), have been used to show that the oxide thickness on the large grains and the small grains are the same thickness. Such data are presented in Figure 14, which shows AES depth-compositional profile data for intra- and intergrain regions, taken for both large- and small-grain areas for polycrystalline Si samples oxided for 1 hr at 140°C. In these cases, a higher-resolution (1500-Å diameter) AES probe was used to obtain better spatial resolution. Profiles (a) and (b) in Figure 14 compare the oxide thicknesses over a large single grain and small single grain, respectively. The thickness and interface regions are effectively the same. Under the same AES experimental conditions, the comparative depth profiles over grain boundaries are shown in Figure 14(a′) [for the grain boundary adjacent to the grain measured in Figure 14(a)] and Figure 14(b′) [for that adjacent to the grain of Figure 14(b)]. The change in the sputtering time axis should be noted. These AES depth-profile data show the penetration of the oxide down the grain. The XPS data also show that the effective oxide thickness is greater for the grain boundary region than for the grain (Figure 13a). At $\theta = 11°$, the SiO$_2$ peak is far more pronounced than for the corresponding case in Figure 13a. The transition layer peak at 101.1 eV becomes evident at $\theta = 50°$. At $\theta = 80°$, the Si(SiO$_2$) 2p peak exceeds the intensity of the elemental Si 2p peak.

The relative thicknesses of the SiO$_2$ and Si^x layers can be calculated on the basis of the angular-resolved data of Figure 13.[51] Assuming that only the *intensities* and not the *shapes* of the Si 2p and Si(SiO$_2$) 2p peaks change significantly

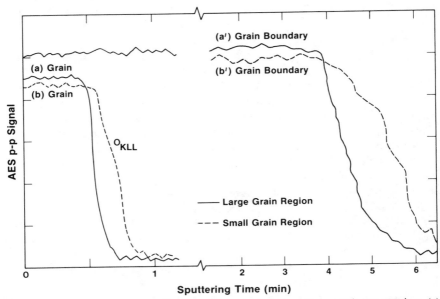

Figure 14. AES depth-compositional profiles comparing oxide growth over grains: (*a*) large grain (8-mm diameter), (*b*) small grain (0.1-mm diameter); and over grain boundaries: (*a'*) adjacent to *a*, (*b'*) adjacent to *b*. AES beam diameter is 1500 Å.

with θ, that the peaks are nearly symmetrical, and that the escape depth (λ) of the electrons is nearly independent of θ, the intensity ratio of the detected Si^x or SiO to the Si XPS signals can be analytically expressed in terms of the emission angle θ. From this relationship and the value of λ, the effective oxide thickness (or transition layer thickness) can be evaluated. Such data are presented in Figure 15 for both grain and grain-boundary regions, using $\lambda = 24$Å,[77,78] the escape depth of the emitted SiO_2 $2p$ electrons. Comparing the grain and grain-boundary regions (at T = 140°C), both the initial higher rate of oxidation and the resulting oxide penetration (greater oxide thickness) are evident. These qualities—oxidation rate and thickness—are more pronounced at grain boundaries than they are for oxide layers grown at higher temperatures. To illustrate this, data for an oxide layer grown at 220°C are shown in Figure 15. The data for oxidation of the grain boundary region shown by Figure 15*c* corresponds (by extrapolation) to an oxidation of a single grain in the 700–800°C range. For comparison, the AES depth-composition data of Figure 14 can be used to estimate the oxide thicknesses. By measurement of sputter-crater depth over the single-grain region, the etching rate was determined to be in the 15–20 Å/min range, making these oxide thickness some 8–12 Å over grains and some 60–90 Å

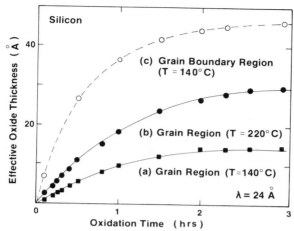

Figure 15. Effective oxide thickness as a function of oxidation time for: (*a*) grain region (*T* = 140°C); (*b*) grain region (*T* = 220°C); and grain boundary region (*T* = 140°C). Here, λ = 24 Å. (From Kazmerski et al.[51])

over the grain boundary. These are consistent with the XPS data presented in Figure 15. The difference in the grain-boundary oxide thickness is explained by the fact that the XPS method measures an effective thickness that encompasses several grain-boundary and grain-region oxides.

Figures 13*a* and 13*b* may also be used to calculate the thickness of the transition layer, Si^x. Using the same technique described above, the thickness of this layer is found to be in the range 4–15 Å for the films of this study. No correlation to oxide growth temperature is apparent. However, the transition layer for the grain boundary regions was consistently in the 12–15 Å range. Overall, the range in the transition layer thickness is more a problem of curve-resolving the Si^x peak at 101.1 eV and obtaining an accurate peak intensity. This is far less of a problem for the dominant Si $2p$ and SiO_2 $2p$ XPS lines.

Therefore, another feature of XPS has been used to investigate a potentially important photovoltaic device processing step. In this, the fact that the photo-ejected electrons are emitted nonuniformly as a function of angle has been exploited to provide information on the initial oxidation of polycrystalline Si. The rate of oxidation and relative oxide thickness have been compared for grain and grain-boundary regions. The oxidation of the grain boundaries occurs at a much higher rate, and the oxide itself penetrates the grain boundary. This is evidenced by a higher effective oxide thickness in these regions, as determined by the angular-resolved XPS method. This oxidation might be used to advantage in polycrystalline solar cells. Since the grain boundaries have a higher rate of initial oxidation, it is possible that this oxide could be used to passivate these regions. Recently, solar cells have been fabricated on small-grain ($\sim$35-μm grain diameter), p-type 25-μm-thick polycrystalline Si films grown by chemical vapor deposition. As-grown polycrystalline Si substrates were used as control samples. Another set were oxidized at 140°C for 20 min as described previously. The oxygen was then sputter etched to both control and oxidized samples subjected to a shallow P-diffusion (n $\sim 10^{18}$, junction depth = 0.25-μm). All six control substrates experienced shorting, with the phosphorus penetrating the grain boundaries. Four of the six oxygen-processed substrates exhibited photovoltaic activity, with efficiencies between 2.3% and 4.6% under 100 mW/cm^2 illumination. Although these *initial* device studies are not conclusive, the results show potential for this passivation scheme. These results also have some impact on metal–insulator–semiconductor solar cells using polycrystalline solar cells. Since these devices typically use a thin (20-30 Å) oxide layer of which uniformity in thickness is critical,[80-83] the enhanced oxidation at grain boundaries reported herein must be considered.

4. SUMMARY AND CONCLUSIONS

Four examples covering four separate solar cell materials have been presented to illustrate the usefulness and utility of XPS as used in conjunction with other surface analysis methods in the investigation of photovoltaic device problems:

1. The application of XPS—in conjunction with AES depth compositional profiling—to identify the formation of a semiconductor (Mg_3P_2) at the interface of a presumably Mg/Zn_3P_2 Schottky barrier. This identification confirms that the resulting device is a heterojunction, in agreement with the electrical and optical characteristics.

2. XPS, complementing SIMS profile data, has shown a significant interfacial chemical reaction between Au and GaAs at room temperature in these metal–semiconductor solar cells. The XPS studies identified the formation of Ga_2Au at the interface and showed that this region is the basis for lower barrier heights and device degradation at higher temperatures.

3. Low-temperature wet and dry oxides and their interfaces with polycrystalline InP have been examined using AES, SIMS, XPS, and EBIC. The dry oxides were shown to be more uniform in composition, and XPS was used to catalog a number of the impurities and compounds in these layers. Elemental P was detected at the interface regions of both oxide types using XPS. Some evidence of impurity accumulation at grain boundaries was provided by the surface analysis in conjunction with microelectrical characterization by EBIC.

4. Angular-resolved XPS was used to investigate the initial oxidation of polycrystalline Si. These data confirm that the oxide initially penetrates the boundary regions. In addition, the angular-resolved XPS measurements have been quantified to provide the effective thicknesses of the oxides and transition region, both for grains and grain boundaries.

Overall, XPS is an important analytical and diagnostic tool which is only beginning to show its importance to these photovoltaic device studies. The constraints imposed upon solar cell cost and areal production, as well as the ambitious economic and performance goals, provide a large field of interest and research for the surface microanalyst. Although no *single* technique is sufficient to solve the manh problems that confront this technology, the large number of device and materials problems that involve both composition and chemistry assure the required role of XPS in the evolution of photovoltaics as a viable energy alternative.

REFERENCES

1. For general information on the status of photovoltaic research, see: (a) *Proceedings of the IEEE Photovoltaic Specialists Conference,* Vols. 1–15, IEEE, New York, 1965–1981; (b) H. Hovel, *Solar Cells,* Academic Press, New York, 1975; (c) L. L. Kazmerski, in *Solar Materials Science,* L. Murr, Ed., Academic Press, New York, 1980, pp. 489–584; (d) W. D. Johnston, Jr., *Solar Voltaic Cells,* Dekker, New York, 1980.

2. P. D. Maycock, *Proceedings of the 14th IEEE Photovoltaic Specialists Conference, San Diego,* IEEE, New York, 1980, pp. 6–12; and *National Photovoltaic Program Plan,* U.S. Dept. of Energy, Division of Solar Energy, DOE/ET-0035(78) (Mar. 1978).

3. See, for example, D. Lichtman, in *Methods of Surface Analysis,* A. W. Czanderna, Ed., Elsevier, New York, 1975, pp. 39–63.

4. R. W. Grant and R. M. Housley, in *Electron and Positron Spectroscopies in Materials Science and Engineering,* O. Buck, J. K. Tien, and H. L. Marcus, Eds., Academic Press, New York, 1979, pp. 219–240.

5. W. M. Riggs and M. J. Parker, in *Methods of Surface Analysis,* A. W. Czanderna, Ed., Elsevier, New York, 1975, pp. 103–158.

6. P. F. Kane and G. B. Larrabee, *Characterization of Solid Surfaces,* Plenum Press, New York, 1974.

7. W. Dekeyser, L. Fiermans, G. Vanderkelen, and J. Vennik, Eds., *Electron Emission Spectroscopy,* Reidel, Amsterdam, 1973.

8. C. R. Brundle and A. D. Baker, Eds., *Electron Spectroscopy: Theory, Techniques, and Applications,* Vol. 1, Academic Press, New York, 1977.

9. T. A. Carlson, *Photoelectron and Auger Spectroscopy*, Plenum Press, New York, 1975, pp. 1–278.

10. L. L. Kazmerski, in *Scanning Electron Microscopy/1980/I*, O. Johari, Ed., SEM Inc., AMF O'Hare, Illinois, 1980, pp. 455–468.

11. J. M. Morabito and R. K. Lewis, in A. W. Czanderna, Ed., *Methods of Surface Analysis*, Elsevier, New York, 1975, pp. 279–328.

12. A. Joshi, L. E. Davis, and P. W. Palmberg, in *Methods of Surface Analysis*, A. W. Czanderna, Ed., Elsevier, New York, 1975, pp. 163–168.

13. D. W. Hoffman, I. S. T. Tsong, and G. L. Power, *J. Vacuum Sci. Technol.*, 17, 239 (1980).

14. L. L. Kazmerski, in *Stability of (Thin Film) Solar Cells and Materials*, D. Sawyer, Ed., National Bureau of Standards Spec. Publ. 400-58, U. S. Dept. of Commerce, Washington, D.C., 1979, pp. 30–40.

15. D. Gupta, D. R. Campbell, and P. S. Ho, in *Thin Films, Interdiffusion and Reactions*, J. M. Poste, K. N. Tu, and J. W. Mayer, Eds., Wiley, New York, 1978, pp. 161–242.

16. A. Catalano, M. Bhushan, and N. Convers-Wyeth, *Proceedings of the 14th IEEE Photovoltaic Specialists Conference, San Diego*, IEEE, New York, 1980, 641–646.

17. P. J. Lin-Chung, *Phys. Stat. Solidi*, B87, 309 (1980).

18. E. A. Fagen, *J. Appl. Phys.*, 50, 6505 (1979).

19. N. Convers-Wyeth and A. Catalano, *J. Appl. Phys.*, 50, 1403 (1979).

20. See, for example, *Commodity Data Summaries*, U. S. Dept. of the Interior, Bureau of Mines, Washington, D.C., 1977.

21. A Catalano and M. Bhushan, *Appl. Phys. Lett.*, in press (1980).

22. L. L. Kazmerski, P. J. Ireland, and A. Catalano, *J. Vacuum Sci. Technol.*, 18, 368 (1981).

23. D. Briggs, Ed., *Handbook of X-ray and Photoelectron Spectroscopy*, Heyden, London, 1978, p. 388.

24. H. Hovel, *Solar Cells*, Academic Press, New York, 1977, pp. 113–125.

25. R. J. Stirn and Y. C. M. Yeh, *Appl. Phys. Lett.*, 27, 95 (1975).

26. P. Dapkus, R. D. Dupuis, R. D. Yingling, J. J. Yang, W. I. Simpson, L. A. Moudy, R. E. Johnson, A. G. Campbell, H. M. Manasevit, and R. P. Ruth, *Proceedings of the 13th IEEE Photovoltaics Specialists Conference, Washington, D.C.*, IEEE, New York, 1978, pp. 960–965.

27. H. T. Yang, D. L. Miller, Y. D. Shen, D. D. Edwall, and J. S. Harris, *Proceedings of the 14th IEEE Photovoltaics Specialists Conference, San Diego*, IEEE, New York, 1980, pp. 1333–1337.

28. R. J. Stirn and Y. C. M. Yeh, *IEEE Trans. Electron Devices*, ED-24, 476 (1977).

29. P. J. Grunthaner, R. P. Vasquez, and F. J. Grunthaner, in *High Efficiency Thin Film GaAs Solar Cells*, R. J. Stirn, Ed., Jet Propulsion Laboratory,

Pasadena, Cal. (Rept. 5030-255), 1979, pp. B1–23; also, *J. Vacuum Sci. Technol.* **16**, 1443 (1979).

30. A. K. Sinha and J. M. Poate, in *Thin Films: Interdiffusion and Reactions (Electrochemical Society Series)* J. M. Poate, K. N. Tu, and J. W. Mayer, Eds., Wiley–Interscience, New York, 1978, pp. 407–432.

31. J. M. Waldrop and R. W. Grant, *Appl. Phys. Lett.*, **34**, 630 (1979).

32. G. Y. Robinson, *J. Vacuum Sci. Technol.*, **13**, 884 (1976).

33. H. M. Day, A. Christou, and A. C. Macpherson, *J. Vacuum Sci. Technol.*, **14**, 939 (1977).

34. A. Smith and P. Mark, *J. Vacuum Sci. Technol.*, **15**, 1344 (1978).

35. P. W. Chye, I. Lindau, P. Pianetta, C. M. Garner, C. Y. Su, and W. E. Spicer, *Phys. Rev.*, **B18**, 5545 (1978).

36. L. L. Kazmerski and P. J. Ireland, *Surface Interface Anal.*, **1**, 144 (1979).

37. R. E. Watson, J. Hudis, and M. Perlman, *Phys. Rev.*, **134**, 4139 (1971).

38. See, for example, A. G. Milnes and D. L. Feucht, *Heterojunctions and Metal-Semiconductor Junctions,* Academic Press, New York, 1972, pp. 156–170.

39. A. Christou, *Solid-State Electronics,* **22**, 141 (1979).

40. See, for example, *Proceedings of the Photovoltaics Adv. R&D Annual Meeting, Denver,* SERI, Golden, Colo., 1979; ibid., Colorado Springs, Colo., 1980.

41. L. L. Kazmerski, P. J. Ireland, P. Sheldon, T. L. Chu, S. S. Chu, and C. L. Lin, *J. Vacuum Sci. Technol.*, **17**, 1061 (1980).

42. A. W. C. Lin, N. R. Armstrong, and T. Kuwana, *Anal. Chem.*, **49**, 1228 (1977).

43. C. D. Wagner, in *Handbook of X-ray and Photoelectron Spectroscopy,* D. Briggs, Ed., Heyden, London, 1977, Chap. 7.

44. See, for example, R. C. Weast, Ed., *Handbook of Chemistry and Physics,* CRC Press, Cleveland, 1978–1979, pp. 13–124, D-71.

45. C. D. Wagner, W. M. Riggs, L. E. Davis, J. F. Moulder, and G. E. Muilenberg, *Handbook of X-ray Photoelectron Spectroscopy,* Perkin-Elmer Corporation, Physical Electronics Division, Eden Prairie, Minn., 1979, pp. 116, 173.

46. C. W. Wilmsen and R. W. Kee, *J. Vacuum Sci. Technol.*, **15**, 1513 (1978).

47. L. L. Kazmerski, *Proceedings of the 14th IEEE Photovoltaic Specialists Conference, San Diego,* IEEE, New York, 1980, pp. 202–207.

48. C. H. Seager and D. S. Ginley, *Appl. Phys. Lett.*, **34**, 337 (1979).

49. C. H. Seager and G. E. Pike, *Appl. Phys. Lett.*, **35**, 709 (1979).

50. J. L. del Valle, C. Flores, and F. Duenas, *Proceedings of the 14th IEEE Photovoltaic Specialists Conference, San Diego,* IEEE, New York, 1980, pp. 202–207.

51. L. L. Kazmerski, O. Jamjoum, P. J. Ireland, and R. L. Whitney, *J. Vacuum Sci. Technol.,* **18**, 960 (1981).

52. C. R. Helms, *J. Vacuum Sci. Technol.,* **16**, 608 (1979).

53. J. Maserjian, *J. Vacuum Sci. Technol.,* **11**, 996 (1974).

54. T. H. DiStefano, *J. Vacuum Sci. Technol.,* **13**, 856 (1976).

55. W. C. Harrington, R. E. Honig, A. M. Goodman and R. Williams, *Appl. Phys. Lett.,* **27**, 644 (1975).

56. R. A. Clark, R. L. Tapping, M. A. Hopper and L. Young, *J. Electrochem. Soc.,* **122**, 1347 (1975).

57. F. J. Grunthaner and J. Maserjian, *IEEE Trans. Nuc. Sci.,* **NS-24**, 2108 (1977).

58. J. Blanc, C. J. Buiocchi, M. S. Abrahams and W. E. Ham, *Appl. Phys. Lett.,* **20**, 120 (1977).

59. O. L. Krivanek, T. T. Sheng and D. C. Tsui, *Appl. Phys. Lett.,* **32**, 437 (1978).

60. J. S. Johannessen and W. E. Spicer, *J. Appl. Phys.,* **47**, 3028 (1976).

61. J. S. Johannessen and W. E. Spicer, *J. Vacuum Sci. Technol.,* **13**, 849 (1976).

62. S. I. Raider and R. Flitsch, *IBM J. Devel.,* **22**, 294 (1978).

63. C. R. Helms, Y. E. Strausser and W. E. Spicer, *Appl. Phys. Lett.,* **32**, 767 (1978).

64. L. C. Feldman, P. J. Silverman, J. S. Williams, T. E. Jackman and I. Stensgaard, *Phys. Rev. Lett.,* **41**, 1396 (1978).

65. G. Hollinger, Y. Jugnet, P. Pertosa, L. Porte and T. M. Duc, *Proceedings of the 7th International Vacuum Congress and 3rd International Conference of Solid Surface,* (Vienna), pp. 2220–2232 (1977).

66. T. Hattori and T. Nishina, *Surface Sci.* **86**, 555 (1979).

67. T. D. Burleigh, S. Wagner and T. F. Ciszek, *Solar Cells,* **1**, 272 (1979).

68. R. P. Vasquez and F. J. Grunthaner, *Surface Sci.* **99**, 681 (1980).

69. A. Redondo, W. A. Goddard, C. A. Swarts and T. C. McGill, *J. Vacuum Sci. Technol.,* **19**, 498 (1981).

70. D. Briggs in *Handbook of X-ray and Photoelectron Spectroscopy,* D. Briggs, Ed., Heyden, London, 1978, pp. 158–167.

71. J. T. J. Huang and J. W. Rabalais, in *Electron Spectroscopy-Theory, Techniques and Applications,* Vol. 2, C. R. Brundle and A. D. Baker, Eds., Academic Press, New York, 1978, pp. 225–256.

72. D. G. Mitchell, K. Aldous, and E. Canelli, *Anal. Chem.,* **49**, 1235 (1977).

73. A. F. Carley and R. W. Joyner, *J. Electron Spectr.,* **13**, 341 (1978).

74. T. F. Ciszek, G. H. Schwuttke, and K. H. Yang, *J. Crystal Growth,* **46**, 527 (1979).

75. T. F. Madey, *Surface Sci.,* **33**, 355 (1972).

76. C. D. Wagner, W. M. Riggs, L. E. Davis, J. F. Moulder, and G. E. Muilenberg, *Handbook of X-ray Photoelectron Spectroscopy*, Perkin-Elmer Corporation, Physical Electronics Division, Eden Prairie, Minn., 1979, pp. 52, 53.

77. A. Ishizaka, S. Iwata, and U. Kamigaki, *Surface Sci.*, **84**, 355 (1979).

78. A. Ishizaka and S. Iwata, *Appl. Phys. Lett.*, **35**, 71 (1980).

79. D. E. Aspnes and J. B. Theeten, *Phys. Rev. Lett.*, **43**, 1046 (1979); also F. J. Grunthaner, *Phys. Rev. Lett.*, **43**, 1683 (1979).

80. M. A. Green, R. B. Godrey, M. R. Willisen, and A. W. Blakers, *Proceedings of the 14th IEEE Photovoltaic Specialists Conference, San Diego, IEEE,* New York, 1980, pp. 684–687.

81. D. L. Pulfrey, *IEEE Trans. Electron Develop.*, **Ed-25**, 1308 (1975).

82. W. A. Anderson, A. E. Delahoy, and R. A. Milano, *J. Appl. Phys.*, **45**, 3913 (1974).

83. G. Cheek, *Solar Cells,* **1**, 405 (1980).

CHAPTER

5

ANALYSIS OF CORROSION FILMS USING XPS: ADVANTAGES AND LIMITATIONS*

N. S. McIntyre

Nuclear Waste Management Division
Department of Nuclear Energy
Brookhaven National Laboratory
Upton, New York

*Work performed under the auspices of the U.S. Nuclear Regulatory Commission.

1. INTRODUCTION

The study of corrosion processes has just recently begun to be assisted by the widespread availability of x-ray photoelectron spectroscopy [XPS, or electron spectroscopy for chemical analysis (ESCA)]. Aqueous corrosion of a material often involves surface chemical changes such as oxidation, diffusion, hydration, and precipitation. To identify corrosion mechanisms, the researcher would be greatly assisted by knowledge of the structure of surface oxides and hydroxides, as well as film thickness and the distribution of individual oxide and metallic phases. Since XPS is surface sensitive and is often capable of determining the oxidation state of an element, it might be thought that the technique would have been rapidly adopted by the corrosion science community. Some of the reasons for the more cautious acceptance of the technique are discussed in this chapter, along with its major advantages compared to other surface techniques. A review of the past applications of XPS to aqueous corrosion studies of the major structural alloying elements is given, and some examples of corrosion studies from the author's laboratory are discussed in more detail to illustrate the potential of XPS for chemical structural identification. The reader is also referred to an earlier review by Castle.[1]

2. ADVANTAGES OF XPS

2.1. Chemical Effects

The basis of the chemical shift of a core photoelectron peak is the change in electrostatic potential on the core electron when valence electron charge density is accepted or withdrawn from the atom.[2] Thus, a relationship exists between the binding energy and the chemical state of the element. The presence of oxidized corrosion product elements can usually be clearly distinguished from the same elements as reduced metals, on the basis of their chemical shifts. Often, it is also possible to differentiate oxides of differing valence (e.g., CrO_4^{2-} and Cr_2O_3) or oxide from hydroxide [e.g., NiO from $Ni(OH)_2$]. The chemical structure also influences other photoelectron peak structures such as shakeup peaks, multiplet splitting, and Auger-electron lineshape. This fact has been useful for characterizing mixed oxide structures and many additional changes in oxidation states. Much of the detail of the spectroscopic lineshapes and chemical shifts, which are characteristic of different corrosion species, unfortunately has not been tabulated in a form that is readily interpretable by corrosion researchers. The characteristic spectroscopic changes are generally not large, and the reported data in the literature often are in conflict or have error limits that are too large to be useful. This situation will improve as energy calibration procedures become more standardized and methods for a more accurate definition of peak shape and position are developed. At present, the *Handbook of X-ray Photoelectron Spectroscopy*[3] has one of the most complete compilations of chemical shift data on compounds of interest to corrosion scientists (i.e., oxides of the structural elements iron, nickel, chromium, cobalt, copper, and manganese).

2.2. Quantitative Analysis

An absolute quantitative description of a corroded surface is seldom required; the surface region has many heterogeneities and impurities which can vary widely in the region under analysis. However, relative quantitative analysis is often very important and the reliability with which intensities can be converted to relative compositions is a major consideration in the choice of surface technique. XPS has been shown to be capable of yielding good quantitative data on a number of metal alloy and oxide surfaces using an empirical approach based on intensities of elemental standards.[4] A more basic approach[5] relates intensity to the surface elemental composition through the electron mean free path and the photoelectron cross section. This model has been successfully applied to oxide surface compositions[6] and has the advantage of requiring no standards. Although the electron mean free paths could be sensitive to matrix structure on highly oriented surfaces, most corrosion-related surfaces are sufficiently randomly mixed to allow an average mean free path term to be used with accuracy. XPS is considered to be an inherently more accurate quantitative measurement than Auger-electron spectroscopy (AES) since backscattering of the primary electron beam and electron-beam damage can influence the Auger-electron yield. Other surface techniques like secondary-ion mass spectrometry (SIMS) have even more difficulties associated with quantitative analysis.

2.3. Beam Damage

The x-ray source in XPS causes less damage to the surface than any of the other common types of surface-analysis techniques which employ electron or ion beams to "interrogate" the sample. Electron bombardment of oxide surfaces has been shown to cause reduction to the metal,[7] while alkali elements can migrate due to the charge accumulation on the surface.[8] Many surface adsorbates present (OH, H_2O, etc.) are rapidly desorbed under electron bombardment. It should be noted that the x-ray beam has been found to cause some chemical reduction in some higher valence state oxide systems (e.g., $Cu^{2+} \rightarrow Cu^+$, $Co^{3+} \rightarrow Co^{2+}$.[9]

3. LIMITATIONS OF XPS

3.1. Spacial Resolution

In XPS, the surface area sampled is of the order of several square millimeters, as defined by the solid acceptance angle of the electron optics. The irradiating x-x-ray flux normally covers a larger area. By contrast, the minimum area sampled by the most recent scanning Auger microprobes is about 0.05 μm^2, while modern ion microprobes can resolve 1 μm^2 areas.

The low spatial resolution of XPS is a serious handicap in studying some corrosion problems. Corrosion processes by their nature are often localized; many reactions are initiated at surface kinks, grain boundaries, or crevices. Unless such phenomena can be generated artificially and isolated from generalized surface corrosion, it will be difficult to use standard XPS instruments to study localized corrosion chemistry. In certain situations, area masking with beryllium foil can provide a partial solution. New powerful x-ray sources such as synchrotrons, when combined with mechanically rastered mask techniques, could provide the requirements for a micro-XPS system for the study of localized corrosion. Scanning Auger microscopy (SAM) is a very useful auxiliary technique for localized corrosion studies. However, SAM can also encounter its own particular set of difficulties, due to geometry and sample charging, particularly in the study of deep corrosion pits.

3.2. Elemental Sensitivity

The detection sensitivity in XPS is limited by the high background caused by the predominance of energy-degraded electrons in the spectrum. With most commercial x-ray sources and counting times of practical duration (approximately 1 hr), elemental detection limits (signal/noise = 3/1) range between 1.0 and 0.1% of the total composition. This means that many corrosion precursors such as chloride or phosphate are barely or not at all detected by XPS under many circumstances. Unless the count rate can be improved substantially (approximately two orders of magnitude) from its present status, XPS will effectively remain a tool for studying only the major phases in a corrosion system.

3.3. Vacuum Effects

All electron and ion optical surface techniques suffer from the disadvantage of having to be placed in a high-vacuum chamber prior to analysis. The desorption of hydrated species from the surface occurs at varying rates, depending on the chemical or physical forces involved. In any case, an important component of the corrosion film is removed, perhaps resulting in the chemical alteration of oxides themselves. For example, the gelatinous $Fe(OH)_3$ surface present on many corroded steels is identified as FeOOH by XPS as a result of vacuum exposure and description.[10] Efforts to preserve the hydration layer by cooling the sample during pumping are not usually successful since in many spectrometers condensation of vacuum impurities will mask the original surface. Alternative methods for analysis of the hydration layer are nuclear microanalysis (relative hydrogen and oxygen surface concentrations) and reflectance infrared spectroscopy (characteristic OH stretching frequencies).

4. DEPTH PROFILING WITH XPS

Profiling of the corrosion film to a depth greater than 2.0 nm involves ion bombardment or etching of the surface and sequential analysis by XPS. This is very important for corrosion film characterization since, even on thin films, the underlying oxide film often has a different chemical composition than the outer surface layer.

Much has been written of the structural damage imparted by ion beams to oxide surfaces. Some damage has been found to result in chemical alteration of the oxides—severe in some cases and tolerable in others. For example, low-energy argon ion bombardment of oxides of iron results in their decomposition to FeO, but no reduction to metallic iron is detected.[10] Oxides of chromium, iron, and nickel can undergo ion bombardment under specified profiling conditions without being decomposed to the metal. Thus, alloys of these metals can be profiled and the oxides and metallic phases can be distinguished by XPS chemical shifts as the surface oxide film is penetrated. Such detailed analysis of the relationship between different oxide phases is not possible by other surface techniques.

In Figure 1, XPS depth profiles are shown for films grown on an Inconel 600* surface following exposure to oxygenated pH 7 water at 280°C. The concentration and composition of the main alloy constituents nickel, chromium, and iron are plotted cumulatively,[11] showing both metallic and oxide concentrations as a function of depth into the oxide film. As the oxide film is penetrated, the oxide components become less significant, and the proportion of each element in the film reflects the bulk alloy composition.

Initially (Figure 1a) a thin (2-4 nm) chromium oxide–rich oxide develops on the surface along with a mixed nickel–iron oxide. After continued oxidation for several hours, however, the main surface component changes to $Ni(OH)_2$ and the film growth rate increases (Figure 1c). This probably results from saturation of nickel in solution followed by the back precipitation on the alloy surface as an

---

*Inconel 600 (77% Ni, 16% Cr, 7% Fe) is a tradename of INCO Metals Limited, Toronto, Canada.

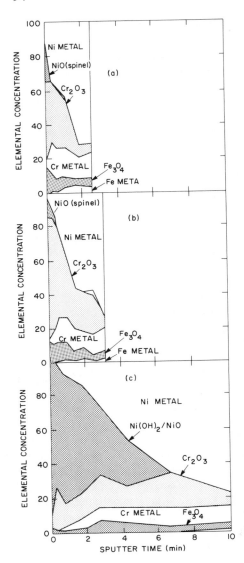

Figure 1. XPS depth profiles of surface films formed on Inconel 600 alloy during initial aqueous oxidation at pH 7 and $T = 280°C$: (*a*) after 0.5-hr exposure; (*b*) after 2-hr exposure; (*c*) after 7-hr exposure.

hydroxide. This nonpassive hydroxide/oxide film continues its growth, while iron and chromium oxide contributions to the film are gradually reduced with increasing exposure.

Depth profile sequences such as these have been shown to be reasonably reproducible in terms of the relative quantities of oxide and metallic phases determined.[12]

5. REVIEW OF AQUEOUS CORROSION STUDIES USING XPS

This section reviews the use of specific photoelectron lines in the determination of corrosion film structure. Relevant elements studied include oxygen, iron, chromium, nickel (major elements, in stainless steel and other alloys), cobalt, copper, manganese, and molybdenum (frequently used as minor alloy constituents).

5.1. Oxygen

The O $1s$ line (~530 eV) has been used extensively in the analysis of oxide surface species. The line has a relatively narrow width and a symmetric shape; this allows more accurate fitting of complex band combinations. An extensive review of O $1s$ binding energies of metal oxides has been reported by Johnson.[13] Although it appears that no simple correlation can be drawn between metal oxide bond character and O $1s$ binding energy (BE), differences between experimental values for some oxides are sufficiently large to allow differentiation. One such case is CuO [BE(O $1s$)] = 529.5 ± 0.2 eV and Cu_2O [BE(O $1s$)] = 530.2 ± 0.2 eV.

Differences between hydroxyl oxygen (OH⁻) and oxide oxygen (O^{2-}) are usually recognized by an O $1s$ shift of 1.0 to 1.5 eV. For example, the oxygen line associated with NiO is located at 529.6 ± 0.2 eV,[14] whereas that for $Ni(OH)_2$ is located at the distinctly higher binding energy of 531.2 ± 0.2 eV. Further, in the mixed oxide–hydroxide compound FeO(OH), contributions from each oxygen can be clearly distinguished in the O $1s$ spectrum.[10] There is some evidence that surface-chemisorbed water is further distinguishable from hydroxyl oxygen, the latter band appearing approximately 1 eV higher in binding energy. The differences in H_2O, −OH, and −O binding energies have been valuable in identifying the nature of passive films on stainless steel[15,16] and iron–chromium alloys.[17] Based partly on the high-binding-energy component of the O $1s$ spectrum, the authors were able to identify the major passivating surface species as CrO(OH) $\cdot nH_2O$. The relative amount of bound water, measured by deconvolution, was found to vary with exposure and with the chromium content.[16] Angular dependence experiments show that the bound water is concentrated at the outer surface.

5.2. Chromium

Chromium species are usually measured using the Cr $2p_{3/2}$ line (~575 eV). Differences between Cr^{3+} species (such as Cr_2O_3), and Cr^{6+} species (such as CrO_4^{2-}) are readily determined from the large 2-eV chemical shift.[18] This difference has been used to determine the composition of electrodeposited chromium oxide surfaces.[19] Chromium(III) oxide (Cr_2O_3) and its hydroxides [$Cr(OH)_3$

and CrO(OH)] also have somewhat different Cr $2p_{3/2}$ binding energies [Δ(BE) = 0.5 eV[20]] ; this has permitted Cr(OH)$_3$ to be identified on a corroded chromium-molybdenum stainless steel surface.

5.3. Manganese

Several manganese oxides of different stoichiometry have been measured by XPS.[21] MnO and MnO$_2$ appear to be distinguishable on the basis of differences in their Mn $2p_{3/2}$ binding energies and peak shapes.[22] No known application of such data has been made to manganese-related corrosion studies.

5.4. Iron

Several XPS studies of iron oxides have been made[10,20,23]: Fe $2p$ photoelectron spectra of ferric and ferrous oxides are particularly complex, because of the large amount of coupling between the core hole created by photoemission and the high spin states of iron. Some of this complexity can be exploited for analytical purposes, since the spectral line shape is quite sensitive to chemical changes. This can be seen in Figure 2, where the Fe $2p_{3/2}$ spectra of α-FeOOH, α-Fe$_2$O$_3$, Fe$_3$O$_4$, and Fe(OOH)$_2$ are compared. The iron(III) hydroxide peak center (Figure 2a) is shifted about 1 eV to higher binding energy than that for alpha Fe$_2$O$_3$. α-Fe$_2$O$_3$ and γ-Fe$_2$O$_3$ (not shown) can be distinguished on the basis of the splitting in the main peak. Magnetite (Fe$_3$O$_4$) contains both Fe(II) and Fe(III), both of which contribute to the Fe $2p_{3/2}$ spectrum in the two overlapping components of Figure 2c. In real-life specimens, unfortunately, Fe$_3$O$_4$ surfaces are not usually as clearly identifiable since exposure to air causes partial oxidation of Fe$_3$O$_4$ to Fe$_2$O$_3$. Finally, some organo-iron compounds which are of interest to corrosion studies can be characterized separately from the oxides. In Figure 2d, ferrous oxalate can be characterized on the bases of its prominent satellite (see arrow). This has been useful for identifying the presence of this species on reactor coolant tubing undergoing chemical decontamination.

Attempts to characterize typical iron sulfide corrosion species have not been as successful. Surface iron sulfides undergo hydrolysis to oxides in air, greatly complicating the spectra. However, FeS and FeS$_2$ are found to have quite different Fe $2p_{3/2}$ spectra, again resulting from differences in the multiplet interactions. FeS$_2$ has a spectrum closely resembling that of metallic iron, whereas FeS is a very broad spectrum centered nearly 2 eV higher than that for FeS$_2$.

Several XPS studies of the interaction of pure iron surfaces with oxygen or water have been reported.[24-26] Iron-chromium alloy corrosion was studied using controlled potential oxidation in 1 M sulfuric acid.[27] XPS showed that at Fe-Cr alloy ratios >0.1, Fe$_3$O$_4$ was the major iron surface species; at lower ratios, a form of Fe$_2$O$_3$ was the major species. Another study of Fe-Mo alloy oxidation

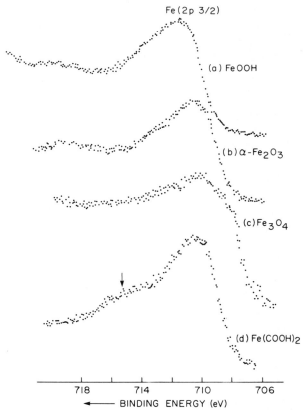

Figure 2. Photoelectron spectra of some typical iron-corrosion compounds. Fe $2p_{3/2}$ spectra are shown for (a) α-FeOOH; (b) α-Fe$_2$O$_3$; (c) Fe$_3$O$_4$; (d) Fe(COOH)$_2$.

in HCl[28] identified iron(III) oxyhydroxide (FeOOH) as a major component of the passive film. Several studies of austenitic stainless steel corrosion[15,29] have identified the iron-corrosion product on passivated surfaces as mainly FeOOH, on the basis of the Fe $2p_{3/2}$ and O $1s$ chemical shifts.

5.5. Cobalt

Several basic XPS studies of cobalt oxides have been reported.[14,30] Shakeup satellite Co $2p_{3/2}$ line structure is the chief method used to distinguish diamagnetic cobalt(III) oxides from paramagnetic cobalt(II) oxides. Also, the cobaltous hydroxide [Co(OH)$_2$] and cobaltous oxide (CoO) are separated by a Co $2p_{3/2}$ chemical shift of about 1 V—sufficient to identify one or the other species on a surface. This has been used to identify $Co(OH)_2$ as the initial species formed during the moist air oxidation of cobalt metal.[31] A study of the aqueous oxidation of a cobalt–chromium alloy[32] also showed that $Co(OH)_2$ was the major corrosion product resulting from hydrothermal reducing conditions. More anodic oxidizing conditions resulted in the production of Co_3O_4.

5.6. Nickel

Unlike cobalt, only one oxidation state of nickel is believed to be present, for all practical purposes, on oxidized nickel surfaces. A chemical shift of approximately 2 eV is found between the Ni $2p_{3/2}$ line positions for NiO and $Ni(OH)_2$, thus facilitating identification of surface $Ni(OH)_2$.[14] The Ni $2p_{3/2}$ spectrum of Ni(II) in different oxide lattices also changes significantly with the chemical structure, again probably due to multiplet interaction.[33] In Figures 3a and 3b, the Ni $2p$ spectra of NiO and the spinel $NiFe_2O_4$ are separated by 1.5 eV, as measured by peak maxima. Also in the $NiFe_2O_4$ spectrum the prominent satellite structure, seen for NiO, has disappeared.

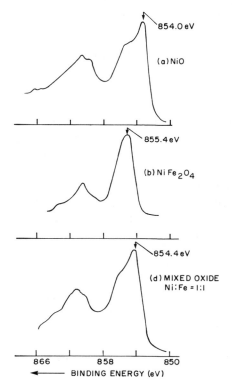

Figure 3.   Photoelectron spectra of some simple and mixed nickel oxides. Ni $2p_{3/2}$ spectra are shown for (a) NiO; (b) $NiFe_2O_4$; (c) mixed iron–nickel oxide (Ni/Fe ratio = 1/1).

Nickel hydroxide has been identified by XPS as a major corrosion species in precipitates from solution during the aqueous oxidation of several nickel alloys.[12,34] Also, a mixed nickel spinel is identified as part of the initial oxide layer formed on the alloy prior to the precipitation of any corrosion products from solution.[12]

5.7. Copper

Copper has been one of the elements most extensively studied by XPS. Interpretation of oxide spectral structure is more straightforward for copper than for other transition metals; also many more applications to corrosion are available.

Two stable oxides of copper [$Cu_2(I)O$ and $Cu(II)O$] in solid-state films when XPS is used.[35] In addition, a cupric hydroxide has been characterized by XPS.[14] All three compounds are likely surface products of the corrosion of copper metal, and their chemical differentiation from the metallic substrate is thus important.

In the case of cuprous oxide, photoelectron spectra are identical to those for copper metal, within ±0.1 eV. However, as initially described by Schoen,[36] the x-ray–induced Auger spectra of copper metal and cuprous oxide ($Cu\,L_3M_{4,5}M_{4,5}$) are significantly different and allow a quantitative characterization[37] of oxide or metal. The $Cu\,L_3M_{4,5}M_{4,5}$ spectra for copper metal, Cu_2O, CuO, and $Cu(OH)_2$ are shown in Figure 4. If contributions from the higher valence oxides are absent, the relative contributions of Cu_2O and metallic copper to the spectrum can be determined by ratioing peak intensities at two different energies.[37] Copper $L_3M_{4,5}M_{4,5}$ Auger spectra of CuO and $Cu(OH)_2$ are both shifted to different kinetic energies, compared to Cu_2O (see Figure 4). However, these peaks are broad and are somewhat more difficult to characterize because of the large number of discrete Auger lines under the envelope. Characterization of CuO and $Cu(OH)_2$ is normally accomplished using the $Cu\,2p_{3/2}$ and $O\,1s$ photoelectron lines, both of which can peak fitted in a relatively straightforward manner. In Figure 5, the $Cu\,2p_{3/2}$ spectra of Cu_2O, CuO, and $Cu(OH)_2$ are compared. The principal $Cu\,2p_{3/2}$ peak maximum for CuO is shifted 1.3 ± 0.2 eV above that for Cu_2O (see arrows), but this maximum is rather poorly defined with respect to the Cu_2O peak because of significant broadening, probably associated with multiplet splitting. The $Cu\,2p_{3/2}$ peak for $Cu(OH)_2$ is shifted 2.5 ± 0.15 eV above that for Cu_2O and is well fitted by a single lineshape with the same width as that for Cu_2O. Cupric compounds are also characterized, in general, by the two strong shakeup peaks located 5–10 eV above the principal $Cu\,2p_{3/2}$ line.[14] The only difference noted between the shakeup spectra of CuO and $Cu(OH)_2$ (see Figure 4) is a change in the relative intensities of the two peaks under the shakeup envelope. The difference is sometimes large enough to be used to suggest the predominance of the oxide or the hydroxide species.

The $Cu\,2p$ shakeup lines have been used by Castle to identify a copper(II)

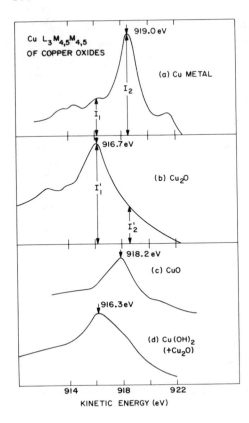

Figure 4.   Cu $L_3M_{4,5}M_{4,5}$ Auger spectra of (a) Cu metal; (b) Cu_2O; (c) CuO; (d) $Cu(OH)_2$ (+ Cu_2O).

oxide formed during the aqueous corrosion of a cupronickel boiler alloy.[38] Also, photoelectron and Auger lines have proven useful in identifying cupric compounds on corroded aluminum brass condenser tubes.[39] The nature of the corrosion-inhibiting mechanism of benztriazole (BTA) on copper has been investigated by two separate groups using XPS.[40,41] Finally, the anodic polarization of a copper electrode in potassium hydroxide solution has been studied as a function of time and anodic potential,[37] showing the initial growth of Cu_2O, followed by the deposition of $Cu(OH)_2$.

5.8. Molybdenum

The corrosion behavior of molybednum, as a component in many stainless steels, has been studied using XPS. Unlike the first-row transition elements, the spectral changes with oxidation state of second-row elements like molybdenum are more predictable and are not accompanied by satellite structure. Thus,

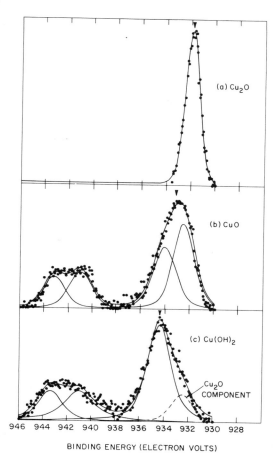

BINDING ENERGY (ELECTRON VOLTS)

Figure 5. Cu $2p_{3/2}$ photoelectron spectra of (a) Cu_2O; (b) CuO; (c) $Cu(OH)_2$.

Mo(IV), and Mo(VI) oxides have been clearly characterized by chemical shifts of the Mo $3d$ line.[42] These have been used for identifying Mo(VI) oxide in the passive film on corroded chromium molybdenum steels.[28,43]

6. CONCLUSION

Most of the applications described above can be termed as exploratory or initial studies. They leave very large subject areas completely unstudied by surface techniques. The combining of electrochemical investigations with XPS chemical shift studies of the electrode surfaces appears particularly promising. A number of experimental systems are now being developed which will facilitate the transfer of samples to the spectrometer without being altered by atmospheric exposure.

REFERENCES

1. J. E. Castle, *Surface Sci.*, **68**, 583 (1977).
2. K. Siegbahn, C. Nordling, A. Fahlmann, R. Nordberg, K. Hamerin, J. Hedman, G. Johansson, T. Bergmark, E. E. Karlsson, I. Lindgren, and B. Lindberg, *Electron Spectroscopy for Chemical Analysis: Atomic, Molecular and Solid State Structure Studies by Means of Electron Spectroscopy*, Almqvist & Wiksells, Stockholm, 1967.
3. C. D. Wagner, W. M. Riggs, L. E. Davis, J. F. Moulder, and G. E. Muilenberg, *Handbook of X-ray Photoelectron Spectroscopy*, Perkin-Elmer Corporation, Physical Electronics Division, Eden Prairie, Minn., 1979.
4. N. S. McIntyre and F. W. Stanchell, *J. Vacuum Sci. Technol.*, **16**, 798 (1979).
5. C. J. Powell, in *Quantitative Surface Analysis of Materials*, N. S. McIntyre, Ed., ASTM-STP-643, American Society for Testing Materials, Philadelphia, 1978.
6. M. P. Seah, *Surface Interface Anal.*, **2**, 222 (1980).
7. J. M. Fontaine, J. P. Durand, and C. LeCressus, *Surface Interface Anal.*, **1**, 196 (1979).
8. C. G. Pantano, D. B. Dove, and G. Y. Onada, *J. Vacuum Sci. Technol.*, **13**, 414 (1976).
9. R. G. Copperthwaite, *Surface Interface Anal.*, **2**, 17 (1980).
10. N. S. McIntyre and D. G. Zetoruk, *Anal. Chem.*, **49**, 1521 (1977).
11. N. S. McIntyre and D. G. Zetoruk, *J. Vacuum Sci. Technol.*, **14**, 181 (1977).
12. N. S. McIntyre, D. Owen, and D. G. Zetoruk, *J. Electrochem. Soc.*, **126**, 750 (1979).
13. O. Johnson, *Chem. Scripta*, **8**, 162 (1975).
14. N. S. McIntyre and M. G. Cook, *Anal. Chem.*, **47**, 2208 (1975).
15. J. E. Castle and C. R. Clayton, *Corrosion Sci.*, **17**, 7 (1977).
16. K. Asami and K. Hashimoto, *Corrosion Sci.*, **19**, 1007 (1979).
17. K. Asami, K. Hashimoto, and S. Shimodaira, *Corrosion Sci.*, **18**, 151 (1978).
18. J. C. Helmer, *J. Electron Spectr.*, **1**, 259 (1972).
19. S. Storp and R. Holm, *Surface Sci.*, **10**, 68 (1977).
20. K. Asami and K. Hashimoto, *Corrosion Sci.*, **17**, 559 (1977).
21. M. Oku, K. Hirokawa, and S. Ikeda, *J. Electron Spectr.*, **7**, 465 (1975).

22. A. Aoki, *Japan J. Appl. Phys.,* **15**, 305 (1976).

23. C. R. Brundle, T. J. Chueng, and K. Wandelt, *Surface Sci.,* **68**, 459 (1977).

24. C. R. Brundle, *Surface Sci.,* **66**, 581 (1977).

25. J. K. Gimzewski, B. D. Padalia, S. Affrossman, L. M. Watson, and D. J. Fabian, *Surface Sci.,* **62**, 386 (1977).

26. G. R. Conner, *Thin Solid Films,* **53**, 38 (1978).

27. K. Asami, K. Hashimoto, and S. Shimodaira, *Corrosion Sci.,* **16**, 387 (1976).

28. K. Hashimoto, M. Naka, K. Asami, and T. Masumoto, *Corrosion Sci.,* **19**, 165 (1979).

29. K. Asami, K. Hashimoto, and S. Shimodaira, *Corrosion Sci.,* **17**, 713 (1977).

30. M. Oku and K. Hirokawa, *J. Electron Spectr.,* **8**, 475 (1976).

31. T. J. Chuang, C. R. Brundle, and K. Wandelt, *Thin Solid Films,* **53**, 19 (1978).

32. N. S. McIntyre, D. G. Zetaruk, and E. V. Murphy, *Surface Interface Anal.,* **1**, 105 (1979).

33. N. S. McIntyre, D. Owen, and D. G. Zetaruk, *Appl. Surface Sci.,* **2**, 55 (1978).

34. N. S. McIntyre, T. E. Rummery, M. G. Cook, and D. Owen, *J. Electrochem. Soc.,* **123**, 1164 (1976).

35. S. W. Gaarenstroom and N. Winograd, *J. Chem. Phys.,* **67**, 3500 (1977).

36. G. Schoen, *J. Electron Spectr.,* **7**, 377 (1972).

37. N. S. McIntyre, D. W. Shoesmith, S. Sunder, and F. W. Stanchell, *J. Vacuum Sci. Technol.,* in press.

38. J. E. Castle, *Nature,* **234PS**, 93 (1971).

39. J. E. Castle, D. C. Epler, and D. B. Peplow, *Corrosion Sci.,* **16**, 145 (1976).

40. R. F. Roberts, *J. Electron Spectr.,* **7**, 197 (1975).

41. P. G. Fox, G. Lewis, and P. J. Boden, *Corrosion Sci.,* **19**, 457 (1979).

42. T. A. Patterson, J. C. Carver, D. E. Leyden, and D. M. Hercules, *J. Phys. Chem.,* **80**, 1702 (1976).

43. K. Hashimoto, K. Asami, and K. Teramoto, *Corrosion Sci.,* **19**, 3 (1979).

CHAPTER

6

ESCA ANALYSIS OF FUNCTIONAL GROUPS ON MODIFIED POLYMER SURFACES

CHARLES N. REILLEY and DENNIS S. EVERHART

Kenan Laboratories of Chemistry
University of North Carolina
Chapel Hill, North Carolina

and

FLOYD F.-L. HO

Hercules Incorporated
Research Center*
Wilmington, Delaware

1. INTRODUCTION

As methods of surface analysis become increasingly sophisticated, it is more and more apparent that chemical reactions taking place at a surface or inter-surface are an extremely complex phenomenon. It is also apparent that the chemical and morphological nature of a surface plays an important role in the

*Hercules Research Center Contribution Number 1729.

surface reaction. The importance of polymer surfaces is no exception. Wettability, polymer–polymer bonding, polymer–metal adhesion, abrasion resistance, coating, triboelectric phenomena, and biocompatibility are several areas where polymer surface chemistry has a prodigious role. An interesting example which illustrates the biochemical significance of a polymer surface is the inherent lack of bio-compatibility of many plastics. Until recently, this bioincompatibility has seriously effected the use of plastics in prosthetics. The surface-induced aggregation of blood platelets on the synthetic implant is believed to initiate events that ultimately cause the adverse response.[1,2] Recently, this problem has been overcome by modifying the polymer surface via introduction of hydrophilic groups.[3,4] A direct correlation between the reduction in platelet adhesion, the increase in biocompatibility, and the extent of surface oxidation was determined.

The chemical properties of a polymer are often determined by the presence or absence of certain surface functional groups. Consequently, methods enabling researchers to selectively analyze specific surface groups would be very useful. Table 1 compares several popular surface-analytical techniques with respect to analysis depth and ability to resolve chemically different groups.[5-16] Highly specialized techniques such as low-energy electron diffraction (LEED), electron-induced desorption (EID), electron energy loss spectroscopy (EELS), and low-energy ion-scattering spectroscopy (ISS) are not considered. The use of these methods for routine analytical applications is currently not widespread, although analytical proliferation of these techniques will likely develop in the near future. Other more classical analytical methods have enough sensitivity to detect surface groups. For example, fluorescence, electron paramagnetic resonance (EPR), and radiolabeling can analyze in the 10^{-10} to 10^{-8} mol/cm^2 range.

Attenuated total internal reflectance (ATIR) is superior for chemical analysis;

TABLE 1. Popular Surface Analytical Techniques

Analytical method	Analysis depth	Chemical resolution	References for comprehensive reviews
Contact Angle	Variable	Poor	5
Attenuated total internal reflectance	~10,000 Å	Good	6,7
ESCA	<100 Å	Moderate	8–11
AES	<50 Å	Moderate	11–13
SIMS	<10 Å	Good	11,14,15
Inelastic electron tunneling spectroscopy	Variable	Good	16

however, ATIR suffers from a relatively large analysis depth. This problem can be partially remedied by multiple internal reflections and digital subtraction of control samples, although ATIR still cannot compete with the more surface-sensitive techniques such as electron spectroscopy for chemical analysis (ESCA), Auger-electron spectroscopy (AES), and secondary-ion mass spectroscopy (SIMS). Static SIMS is extremely sensitive to submonolayer constituents and has been shown useful for polymer analysis.[17,18] SIMS, however, suffers from the poorly characterized effects of ion beams on organic materials. AES is usually not feasible for polymer analysis due to the dire effects of energetic electrons on organic samples. Contact angle measurements are limited to determining the relative hydrophobic or hydrophilic nature of a surface. Inelastic tunneling spectroscopy is well established as a viable surface technique but suffers from being instrumentally cumbersome.

ESCA [or x-ray photoelectron spectroscopy (XPS)] is well suited for studying polymer surfaces. Several recent reviews on ESCA are available,[8-11] and an excellent book edited by Briggs[8] discusses ESCA in some detail. The important advantages and disadvantages of ESCA as applied to polymer analysis have been reviewed by several authors[19-21] and are summarized in Table 2. Clark[21,22] and co-workers have extensively used ESCA to characterize polymer surfaces.

In many important applications, specific modification of the polymer surface is essential. Modification is usually confined to the very surface of the polymer, leaving the bulk properties of the polymer unchanged. For example, surface carbonyl and carboxyl groups are known to be incorporated on polyethylene and polypropylene films with mild dichromate oxidation.[23,24] These func-

TABLE 2. ESCA as Applied to Polymer Surface Analysis

Advantages

Multielemental: rapid qualitative analysis for all elements except H
Surface sensitive: $<100\text{Å}$
Moderate chemical speciation through binding-energy shifts
Semiquantitative ($\pm15\%$)
Allows for depth profiling via angular dependent measurements
Low detection limits
Modest sample requirements

Disadvantages

Sample charging
Frequent sample decomposition
Poor lateral resolution along surface plane
Limited resolution for many elements

tionals are at least in part responsible for the increased wettability of the previously hydrophobic surfaces. Surface carbonyls and carboxylates also allow dyeing agents to firmly adhere to polyethylene while the insulating and mechanical properties of the polymer remain essentially unchanged. Numerous reports on the identification and modification of functional groups introduced on polyethylene (PE) and polypropylene (PP) films with chemical oxidation have been made.[23,25-27] Other methods of chemical surface modification are routinely used for a wide variety of purposes.

Surface modification by exposure to glow-discharge (low-temperature) and corona-discharge (high-temperature) plasma is currently receiving considerable attention.[22,28] Plasma modification is useful because it is experimentally simple, easily controlled, and produces drastic alterations in surface chemistry without changing the quality of the "bulk" material. Low-power, glow-discharge plasma modification has been modeled by a two-component (direct and radiative) energy transfer process.[29] The rapid, direct energy transfer is dominated by collisions of ions, neutral species, electrons, and metastables with the substrate and is confined to the outer 10–30 Å of the surface. The slower, radiative transfer process results from the ultraviolet (UV) radiation generated in the plasma volume and establishes a much deeper modification depth. Corona discharges in air are generally more complex than glow discharges in a controlled environment. These electric discharges are popular because they are readily suited for continuous "on-line" application.

Although the details of plasma–surface interactions are complex, it is generally recognized that glow-discharge and corona-discharge plasmas can extensively oxidize a polymer surface.[22,24] Oxidation results from the reaction of surface radicals with reactive intermediates of CO_2, H_2O, and O_2 which are usually ubiquitous in the plasma volume. For inert gas plasmas, scrupulous removal of these gases will significantly reduce surface oxidation and promote higher surface cross-linking efficiencies.[29] Postplasma reactions of surface intermediates with atmospheric gases can introduce additional oxidation products. Functional groups derived from other reactive plasma gases can also be incorporated. Table 3 illustrates some groups which could be expected on nitrogen plasma–modified

**TABLE 3. Some Functional Groups Expected on
Nitrogen-Plasma–Modified Polyethylene**

—OH	$>$O	$>$C=CR$_2$
$>$C=O	—CO$_2$NH$_2$	—N=NR
—CO$_2$H	—C≡N	—NO$_2$
—CO$_2$R	—NH$_2$	$>$C=CHCH$_2$COR

PE. This chapter will examine some problems and some recent advances associated with the ESCA analysis of specific surface functional groups such as those illustrated in Table 3.

2. ESCA ANALYSIS OF MODIFIED POLYMER SURFACES

The ability of ESCA to identify and characterize modified polymer surfaces has been exploited for a variety of purposes. Polymers that contain an electroactive functional group have been coated on electrodes. These chemically modified electrodes have generated considerable interests in attempts to elucidate charge-transfer and electrocatalytic mechanisms.[30] ESCA has proved helpful in characterizing these chemically modified electrodes and has allowed for the detection of electrogenerated products.

ESCA has been useful for studying polymer adhesion. The adhesion of vapor-deposited Ni, Cr, and Cu to polyvinyl alcohol and to plasma-modified polystyrene has been shown to involve a surface oxygen–metal complex.[31-33] The improved adhesion of Teflon after surface grafting of methyl acrylate has been studied,[34] and maximum adhesion results when the fluorocarbon surface is covered with an outer layer of methyl acrylate. In an experimentally related study, acrylic acid was grafted to polypropylene film.[35] The modified surface was able to concentrate metals from dilute solutions, and subsequently these metals were analyzed semiquantitatively with ESCA. The nature of the interface between polyethylene pressed[36] or melted[37] against Al has been characterized with ESCA. Recently, Briggs and Kendall[38] have employed ESCA to study the chemical basis of adhesion for corona-discharge–treated polyethylene.

The use of ESCA to characterize plasma-modified polymer surfaces has received much attention. Surface oxidation introduced with mild exposure to glow-discharge[39] or corona-discharge[38,40] plasma is readily detected on a variety of polymers. ESCA has been used in conjunction with contact angle and surface energy measurements to characterize corona-discharge modification of Mylar,[40] Teflon,[41] and polyethylene.[38] In these studies, the presence of surface alcohols, carbonyls, and carboxyl groups was suggested. The increased biocompatibility of plasma-modified polymers has been studied with ESCA.[3,4]

A particularly noteworthy limitation of ESCA is its inability to resolve chemically similar functional groups. Table 4 illustrates this problem for several carbon-, nitrogen-, and oxygen-containing groups.[42] Typical full width at half-maximum height (FWHM) of the C_{1s} for the CH_2 of polyethylene is 1.2–1.3 eV; monochromatic x-ray radiation would improve the resolution to about 0.6–0.8 eV. Sample charging, however, further complicates the identification of specific functional groups. Charging introduces indeterminant increases in peak widths and results in an increase in binding-energy position. Frequently, these changes in peak shapes and positions are dependent on x-ray exposure time.[43]

TABLE 4. Some Binding-Energy Shifts for C_{1s}, N_{1s}, and O_{1s} ESCA Transitions

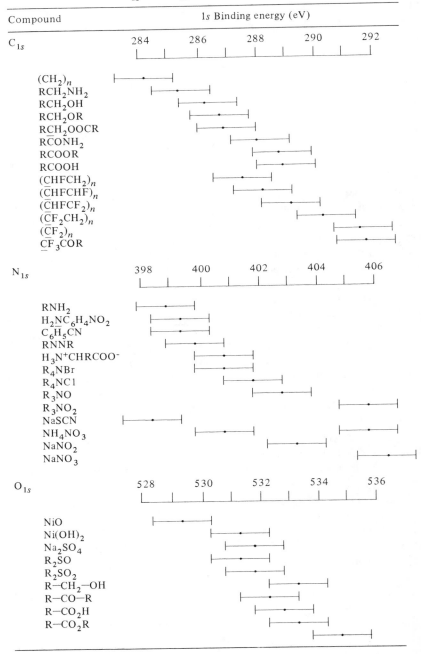

Compound	$1s$ Binding energy (eV)
C_{1s}	284 286 288 290 292
$(CH_2)_n$	
RCH_2NH_2	
RCH_2OH	
RCH_2OR	
RCH_2OOCR	
$R\overline{C}ONH_2$	
$RCOOR$	
$RCOOH$	
$(\overline{C}HFCH_2)_n$	
$(\overline{C}HFCHF)_n$	
$(\overline{C}HFCF_2)_n$	
$(\overline{C}F_2CH_2)_n$	
$(\overline{C}F_2)_n$	
$\overline{C}F_3COR$	
N_{1s}	398 400 402 404 406
RNH_2	
$H_2\overline{N}C_6H_4NO_2$	
$C_6H_5\overline{C}N$	
$RNNR$	
$H_3N^+CHRCOO^-$	
R_4NBr	
R_4NCl	
R_3NO	
R_3NO_2	
$Na\overline{S}CN$	
NH_4NO_3	
$NaNO_2$	
$NaNO_3$	
O_{1s}	528 530 532 534 536
NiO	
$Ni(OH)_2$	
Na_2SO_4	
R_2SO	
R_2SO_2	
$R{-}CH_2{-}OH$	
$R{-}CO{-}R$	
$R{-}CO_2H$	
$R{-}CO_2R$	

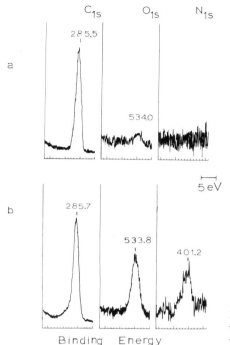

Figure 1. C_{1s}, O_{1s}, and N_{1s} ESCA spectra of (*a*) control polyethylene and (*b*) nitrogen plasma exposed polyethylene.

Various methods have been proposed to compensate for and/or reduce sample charging effects,[44] although the precision of these methods for different laboratories has been questioned.[45]

Pragmatically, ESCA can readily distinguish general chemical classes of functional groups. Reduced organic nitrogen (imines, amines, amides, nitriles, etc.) can be distinguished from the more oxidized nitrates, nitrites, and nitroso compounds. Differentiating carbonyl, carboxylate, and alcoholic oxygens is not possible from O_{1s} ESCA spectra. These oxidized carbon functionals are evident as a high-binding-energy shoulder on the saturated C_{1s} signal but are rarely resolved for unambiguous identification. Fluorinated carbon is easily detected because of the large, high-binding-energy shifts introduced in the C_{1s} signal for carbon covalently bound to fluorine. Consequently, the fluorination of polyethylene[46] and graphite[47] are particularly amendable to study with ESCA. Generally, definitive assignments based on subtle differences in binding energy shifts on insulating samples are dangerous.

The problems of identifying specific functional groups with ESCA are illustrated in Figure 1 for the spectra of polyethylene exposed to radio frequency, inductively coupled nitrogen plasma (PE-N). In contrast to the control, unexposed polyethylene (PE–H), the ESCA spectrum of PE–N shows clear evidence for oxidized carbon and organic nitrogen groups. The widths of the high binding energy C_{1s} shoulder and the width of the O_{1s} spectrum suggests the presence of multiple carbon–oxygen functionals. More specific chemical speciation of the surface groups is not possible.

Several procedures can increase the utility of ESCA for the identification of specific functional groups. These include computer curve fitting, digital subtraction of controls, x-ray-excited Auger lines, and chemical derivatization. Computer curve fitting is the more commonly used resolution enhancement technique.

The principles of curve fitting have received recent review.[48] Choosing a reasonable range of peak widths and expected peak positions, curve fitting attempts to reconstruct the experimental spectrum from a minimum collection of artificially generated composite spectra. To account for the high-binding-energy inelastic loss features present in most ESCA spectra, the composite signals are frequently constructed from either a skewed Gaussian/Lorentzian peak shape or a Gaussian/Lorentzian peak superimposed on an "S" background. A "good fit" is established by varying the widths and positions of the composite spectra to minimize the residual-squares error. It is important to appreciate that curve fitting of ESCA data is inherently not a deconvolution procedure.[9] Curve fitting seldom establishes a unique fit and usually produces a result that is only speculative. Given these restrictions, curve fitting nevertheless can be useful. The utility of fitting increases as knowledge of the surface chemical composition becomes more accurate. For example, resolving the chemically different carbons of polymethyl methacrylate via curve fitting the C_{1s} ESCA spectrum would be a trivial and relatively precise exercise.

The results of curve fitting the C_{1s} spectrum of PE–N are illustrated in Figure 2 and summarized in Table 5. Groups similar to those in Table 1 are suggested.

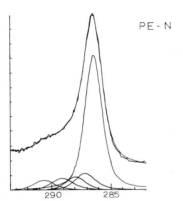

PE - N

290   285

Figure 2. Curve fitting the C_{1s} ESCA spectrum of nitrogen-plasma–modified polyethylene.

TABLE 5. Results of Curve Fitting the C_{1s} Signal
of Polyethylene Exposed to Nitrogen Plasma

Peak	Position[a] (eV)	Width (eV)	Assignment	Percentage total carbon
1	285.0	1.86	CH_2; $C=C$	74
2	286.0	1.80	$C-NH_2$[b]	8
3	286.9	2.06	$C-OH$	8
4	288.1	1.74	$C=O$	5
5	289.4	1.89	CO_2H	5

[a]Reference CH_2 of polyethylene to 285.0 eV.
[b]This peak may be assigned to conjugated carbons such as α,β-unsaturated carbonyls and 1,3-dienes, as well as to carbons containing the amine group.

Difference spectra can also enhance the interpretation of unresolved ESCA spectra. Digitally subtracting a control can often accentuate features otherwise hidden by predominant ESCA signals. Burkstrand[32] used difference spectra to identify a surface metal-oxygen complex on polyvinyl alcohol. Subtraction can also remove the inelastic photoelectron loss features. The difference spectrum resulting from the subtraction of unmodified control polyethylene (PE-H) from PE-N is shown in Figure 3. The oxidized carbon features are clearly accentuated relative to the C_{1s} spectra in Figure 1.

X-ray–excited Auger lines can provide additional information for the identification of chemical states. Auger transitions are useful because they are sensitive to the polarizability of the immediate atomic environment of the emitter. Consequently, Auger signals often show binding-energy shifts significantly larger than their ESCA counterparts. This is especially true for Na, Mg, Cu, Zn, Ag, and Cd.[49, 50] The modified Auger parameter, α', defined as the sum of the kinetic energy of the Auger electron and the photoelectron binding energy, is particularly useful for distinguishing chemical states.[51] A unique advantage of the modified Auger parameter is its insensitivity to sample charging, making the often imprecise methods of charge correction unnecessary. Presently, applica-

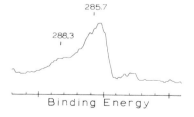

285.7

288.3

Binding Energy

Figure 3. Difference spectrum resulting from the subtraction of the C_{1s} of control polyethylene from the C_{1s} of nitrogen-plasma–modified polyethylene. Both C_{1s} of ESCA signals were charge corrected to 285.0 eV.

tion of the Auger parameter has been limited to inorganic materials, although Wagner[52] has recently outlined its usefulness for the study of oxygen-containing polymers.

3. CHEMICAL DERIVATIZATION OF SURFACE FUNCTIONAL GROUPS

Chemical derivatization is a clever approach enabling researchers to analyze specific surface functional groups with ESCA. Derivatization reagents that contain a unique elemental tag can readily be identified in subsequent ESCA analysis. In principle, these reagents should react selectively and analytically with only the intended functional group. The elemental tag should have a favorable photoelectron cross section and should be stable to ESCA analysis. For example, PE-N containing surface amines would react with pentafluorobenzaldehyde (PFB) to form the Schiff's base derivative via Reaction 1:

$$PE-N + C_6F_5CHO \rightarrow PE-N{=}CHC_6F_5 + H_2O \qquad (1)$$
$$\text{(A)}$$

Pentafluorobenzaldehyde reacts with $1°$ amines and hydrazines but is not expected to react with amides, imines, nitriles, or nitrogen-containing heterocyclics. A F_{1s} signal during subsequent ESCA analysis of **A** would provide strong evidence for surface amines and/or hydrazines on the polymer.

The derivatized polymer has to be rigorously washed to ensure removal of unbound, absorbed reagent. Washing is especially necessary to remove large hydrophobic reagents that are tenaciously soluble in organic polymers. This requires that surface products be securely attached to the polymer and not be removed by repeated solvent extraction. Stability to washing is important and illustrates an intrinsic advantage of covalent tags over ionic derivatives. For example, attempts to form sodium salts via neutralization of surface carboxylic acids with NaOH have been largely unsuccessful.[53] The surface Na^+ concentration is highly irreproducible and strongly dependent on the method used to wash the excess reagent from the sample. The ionic tag is easily removed. Conversely, ester formation of surface carboxylic acids is reproducible and results in a product stable to extensive Soxhlet extraction.

The ESCA spectrum of PE-N treated with 0.1 M pentafluorobenzaldehyde in pentane and subsequently Soxhlet extracted with pentane is shown in Figure 4. A control sample not modified via exposure to N_2 plasma shows no F_{1s} and no N_{1s} signal after treatment with the aldehyde reagent. The nitrogen-plasma-exposed sample shows an eminent F_{1s} signal, a decrease in the N_{1s} area, and an increased area in the high-binding-energy region of C_{1s}. The F/N atomic density is 6.0, slightly higher than the value expected for a surface of fully derivatized

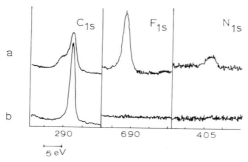

Figure 4. Derivatization to enhance ESCA analysis of surface amines: C_{1s}, F_{1s}, and N_{1s} ESCA spectra of (*a*) PE–N and of (*b*) PE–H after both samples were treated with 0.1 *M* pentafluorobenzaldehyde in pentane and subsequently Soxhlet extracted with pentane.

amines. The reaction of PFB with hydrazines would produce a measurably lower F/N atomic density ratio. The F/N density ratio determined from Figure 4 suggests that most of the nitrogen functions detected on PE–N are primary amines, complementing a previous suggestion that nitrogen plasma introduces amine groups on polyethylene. These surface amines can be protonated (vida infra), and the resulting ESCA spectrum shows a sharp N_{1s} signal with a charge-corrected binding energy of 401.5 eV. This provides additional evidence that hydrazines are not formed on PE–N. Protonated hydrazines would not show a sharp single N_{1s} signal.

In addition to the more positive identification of specific groups, derivatization can extend detection limits. The increased sensitivity is achieved by a stoichiometric and a cross-section enhancement of the elemental tag. For a PFB derivative, the F_{1s}/C_{1s} intensity ratio is expected to be 12 times larger than the N_{1s}/C_{1s} ratio; experimentally, the former ratio is 14 times larger than the N_{1s}/C_{1s} ratio. The quantitative aspects of derivatization/ESCA analysis will be discussed shortly.

Chemical derivatization in conjunction with ESCA analysis is a novel idea. Riggs and Dwight[54] reported the first example of derivatization/ESCA analysis with Br_2/CCl_4 to detect surface unsaturation in chemically modified Teflon. A few years later, Briggs[37] reported the same reaction to detect unsaturation in polyethylene melted against Al. In both these studies, the authors assumed the Br_2/CCl_4 reaction was specific for alkene functionals. Additional use of derivatization/ESCA analysis has only recently been reported.

Briggs and Kendall[38] have used chemical derivatization with ESCA to determine the functional groups important for the autoadhesion of corona-modified polyethylene. These authors suggested NaOH and pentafluorophenylhydrazine (PFPH) for the identification of carboxylate and carbonyl functions respectively.

Problems with NaOH derivatization were noted. From this study, enol–keto tautomerism of surface carbonyls is thought to be important in increasing auto-adhesion. To quantitatively determine surface hydroxyl groups, Hammond[55] suggested the gas phase reaction of trifluoroacetic anhydride (TFAA). As surface standards, this investigator chose random methylmethacrylate–hydroxypropyl-methacrylate copolymers of known ester/hydroxy molar ratios. He found that surface hydroxyl concentrations as determined from ESCA analysis of the TFAA derivative were in excellent agreement with the expected bulk polymer hydroxyl concentration. At a recent ESCA Users' Group Meeting, Wendt and Batich[56,57] presented a collection of ESCA studies using polymer surface derivatization. At an earlier meeting, D. Williams[58,59] reported a collection of derivatization procedures for several common functional groups. Table 6 sum-marizes the previous work reported on derivatization/ESCA methods of analysis.

The present authors have studied a variety of derivatization schemes to identify some specific functional groups on plasma modified and chemically oxidized polyethylene[53] and polypropylene film. These reactions are illustrated in Figure 5. Other reactions not investigated but believed to be useful are suggested in Table 7.

Many of the derivatives presented in Figure 5 and Table 7 have a common familiarity to gas chromatographers who employ electron capture detectors (ECD). Reference to any one of a number of handbooks of derivatives for chromatography[60] can provide many interesting possibilities which may prove useful for derivatization/ESCA analysis. Generally, these chromatographic derivatization reagents contain a stoichiometrically enhanced tag which fortu-itously has a favorable photoelectric cross section, a requisite for the successful analysis with a derivatization/ESCA procedure. Besides gas chromatography with ECD, fluorinated compounds are routinely used in many ^{19}F-NMR (nuclear magnetic resonance) and biochemical applications. At this time, the large availability of fluorine-labeled compounds has not been exploited for use in derivatization/ESCA analysis.

Included in Table 7 are nitroxide and dansyl derivatives which show EPR and fluorescence signals, respectively. These derivatives also contain an elemental ESCA tag. The nitroxide and dansyl groups are especially interesting because they can be analyzed quantitatively by an independent method to substantiate semiquantitative ESCA results. Furthermore, EPR line widths of nitroxide labels are useful for determining rotational correlation times.[61,62] Subsurface ni-troxides should show considerable anisotropy in the lineshapes of their EPR triplet. Fluorescence emission wavelengths are known to depend on the polarity of the environment of the emitter. This should be useful for probing surface modification. For example, the surface of plasma-oxidized polyethylene is hydrophilic in comparison to the interior of the polymer. Accordingly, a shift in fluorescence emission is expected for tags located in the outer hydrophilic and

TABLE 6. Schemes to Derivatize Surface Functional Groups for Subsequent ESCA Analysis

Functional Group	Reagent	Derivatize	Reference
$-\overset{\mid}{C}=\overset{\mid}{C}-$	Br_2/CCl_4	$-\overset{Br}{\underset{\mid}{\overset{\mid}{C}}}-\overset{Br}{\underset{\mid}{\overset{\mid}{C}}}-$	37, 54, 58
	$Hg(OAc)_2$	$-\overset{R-O}{\underset{\mid}{\overset{\mid}{C}}}-\overset{Hg(OAc)}{\underset{\mid}{\overset{\mid}{C}}}-$	58
$-OH$	$Cl-CO-C_6H_3(NO_2)_2$	$-O-CO-C_6H_3(NO_2)_2$	58
	$(CF_3CO)_2O$	$-O-CO-CF_3$	55
$-\overset{O}{\overset{/\backslash}{C-C}}-$	HCl	$-\overset{\mid}{C}(OH)\overset{\mid}{C}(Cl)-$	58
$-\overset{\mid}{C}=O$	$RNHNH_2$	$-\overset{\mid}{C}=NNHR$	58
	$C_6F_5NHNH_2$	$-\overset{\mid}{C}=NNHC_6F_5$	38
$-CH_2-\overset{\mid}{C}=O$	Br_2	$-\overset{Br}{\underset{Br}{\overset{\mid}{C}}}-\overset{\mid}{C}=O$	38
$-CO_2H$	$NaOH$	$-CO_2^-Na^+$	38,58
	$BaCl_2$	$(-CO_2^-)_2Ba^{2+}$	35
	$AgNO_3$	$-CO_2^-Ag^+$	58
	$TlOCH_2CH_3$	$-CO_2Tl$	56,57
$-NH_2$	$CH_3CH_2SCOCF_3$	$-NHCF_3$	59
	CS_2	$-NHCSSH$	58
$-SH$	$AgNO_3$	$-SAg$	58

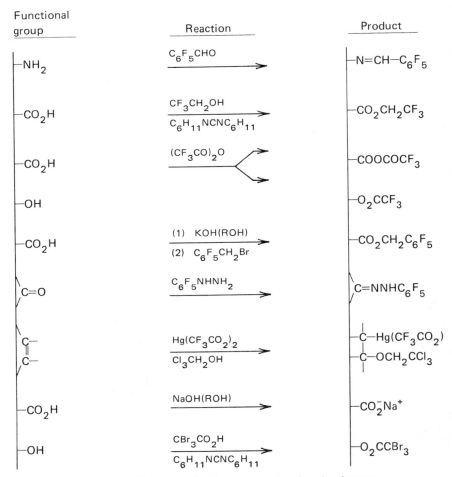

Figure 5. Chemical derivatization of surface functional groups.

in the inner hydrophobic regions of the polymer. Whitesides et al.[23] have observed this shift in fluorescence emission for chemically oxidized polyethylene. Radiolabeled derivatives will also allow independent, quantitative measurements. We believe that EPR, fluorescence, and radiolabeled derivatives which contain an ESCA tag can provide a wealth of information in polymer surface analysis.

One additional observation is reported. On several occasions, the ESCA spectrum of PE-Ar revealed small concentrations of Ar in the polymer. A similar observation has recently been reported by Ullevig and Evans,[63] who studied the Ar etching of polystyrene deposited on a quartz crystal microbalance. We believe that the Ar observed in PE–Ar results from Ar implanted in polyethylene crystallites. The amorphous regions of polyethylene are too dynamic to retain implanted Ar. This interpretation is interesting because it suggests a convenient and unique method of determining surface crystallinity.

TABLE 7.   Some Potentially Important Surface Derivatizations

(A)   Specific Surface Derivatives

Functional group	Reagent	Known interferences[a]
$-\overset{\mid}{C}=\overset{\mid}{C}-$	OsO_4^{2}	
$-OH$	$C_6F_5(CH_3)_2SiCl$	$-CO_2H$
$-\overset{\mid}{C}=O$	$C_6F_5CH_2ONH_2 \cdot HCl$	
$-NH_2/-NHR$	C_6F_5NCS	$-NNH_2$
NR_3	$C_6F_5CH_2OCOCl$	$-OH$
$-SH$	$[C_6H_3(NO_2)(CO_2Na)-S]_2$	

(B)   Some Multifunctional Derivatives

Functional group	Reagents	Derivatives
$-CO_2H$ $-OH$	(1) CCl_3CH_2OH/BF_3 (2) $[CF_3(CF_2)_2CO]_2O$	$-CO_2CH_2CCl_3$ $-O_2C(CF_2)_2CF_3$
$-OH$ $-NH_2$	(1) $C_6F_5(CH_3)_2SiCl$ (2) C_6Cl_5CHO	$-OSi(CH_3)_2C_6F_5$ $-N=CHC_6Cl_5$
$-OH$ $-\overset{\mid}{C}=O$ $-CO_2H$	$(CH_3CH_2)_2NSF_3{}^b$	$-F$ $-\overset{\mid}{C}F_2$ $-COF$

TABLE 7. (continued)

(C)   Derivatives Which Allow for Other Spectroscopic Identification

Functional group	Reagent	Additional analysis mode
—OH $-\overset{\mid}{C}=O$ —CO$_2$H —NH$_2$	 for —OH; X = CO$_2$H[c] $-\overset{\mid}{C}=O$; NH$_2$ —CO$_2$H; OH[3] —NH$_2$; C=O	EPR
—NH$_2$ $-\overset{\mid}{C}=O$	 for NH$_2$; X = Cl $-\overset{\mid}{C}=O$; NHNH$_2$	Fluorescence

[a]Interferences expected from analogous solution reactions.
[b]An especially dangerous reagent. Great caution is required in handling.
[c]Coupling reaction which requires dicyclohexylcarbodiimide.

4. SELECTIVITY OF DERIVATIZATION REACTIONS: THE NEED FOR A STANDARD SURFACE

The success of chemical derivatization/ESCA methods depends on the selectivity of the derivatization reactions. Reactions of interfering functional groups should be characterized and accounted for if an accurate qualitative analysis is to be achieved. This requires that the selectivity of each reaction should be evaluated with surfaces containing a collection of known functional groups. Unfortunately, standard polymer surfaces are often difficult to obtain.

For an initial approximation, the selectivity of surface reactions can be considered similar to the selectivity of solution analogs. Given this assumption, the reactions of pentafluorophenylhydrazine (PFPH) and mercuric trifluoroacetate should be selective for carbonyl and olefinic groups, respectively.[60] The coupling of an acid and an alcohol to form a labeled carboxylate ester should allow for the selective identification of surface carboxylic acids and surface alcohols.[60] Pentafluorobenzylbromide (PFBBr) reacts with carboxylate salts and alcohols to form the corresponding esters and ethers respectively. Favorable reaction rates of pentafluorobenzylbromide with carboxylate salts can be exploited to selectively determine carboxylic acids in the presense of alcohols.[60] In contrast, trifluoroacetic anhydride and acid chlorides react rather indiscriminately with a variety of compounds containing an active hydrogen.

Attempts to increase the selectivity of anhydride and acid chloride reagents have relied on post derivatization hydrolysis of surface products. For example, trifluoroacetic anhydride will react with alcohols and carboxylic acids as follows:

$$
\begin{vmatrix} -OH \\ -CO_2H \end{vmatrix} + (CF_3CO)_2 \rightarrow \begin{vmatrix} -O-CO-CF_3 \\ -CO-O-CO-CF_3 \end{vmatrix} \tag{2}
$$

Hydrolysis of the mix anhydride allows for the identification of surface alcohols. Similarly, the selective hydrolysis of pentafluorobenzyl esters should allow for the identification of pentafluorobenzyl ethers.

Reaction selectivity of surface groups may not always be accurately predicted from solution chemistry analogs. It is, therefore, necessary to characterize surface reactions with standard polymers which contain specific functional groups. The wide variety of commercially available polymers offers an obvious choice of standard surfaces. For example, polyvinyl alcohol might be useful for evaluation of reactions with the alcohol function. Copolymers containing several functional groups are available and could be used to characterize selectivity in the presence of several groups. Although this approach appears straightforward, commercial polymers have several disadvantages that complicate their use as standard

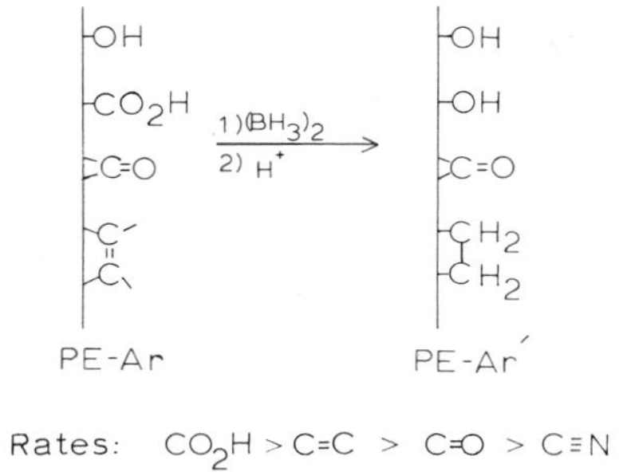

Figure 6. Selective reduction of surface carboxylic acids and surface olefins with diborane/THF.

Rates: $CO_2H > C=C > C=O > C\equiv N$

surfaces. Commercial polymers often contain residual surface oxidation and/or contamination introduced during processing and handling. In addition, surface segregation of functional groups in a copolymer can make the surface stoichiometrically different than the bulk. Blooming of bulk additives to the surface can also occur.

These problems can be remedied by synthesizing and carefully purifying a polymer just before use in a derivatization scheme. This approach has been advocated by Hammond et al.,[55] reportedly with successful results. This method suffers, however, because it requires the custom synthesis of a large number of polymers.

An alternative approach to generating standard polymer surfaces is to selectively reduce or oxidize surface functional groups with reagents known to be effective for this purpose. Figure 6 illustrates how selective reduction of CO_2H and olefins can be achieved by differences in reduction rates.[23,64] Mild reduction with 0.1 M diborane/THF (tetrahydrofuran) converts CO_2H to alcohols without affecting the concentration of carbonyls. Extensive reduction with diborane will reduce carbonyls to alcohols. Relative to an unreduced surface, the derivatization of a mildly reduced surface should reveal an increase in alcohols and no change in the carbonyl concentration. No carboxylates should be detected on the reduced sample with a carboxylate-specific derivative. Reductions in the surface olefin concentration could be expected because olefins and carboxylic acids are reduced with similar rates. Marked deviation from these expected results will raise serious questions concerning the selectivity of the derivatization reactions employed.

Before examining the derivatization/ESCA analysis of reduced and unreduced polyethylene, it is instructive to consider what can be learned from curve fitting the C_{1s} ESCA spectra of these surfaces. Figure 7 illustrates the C_{1s} spectra of control polyethylene (PE-H), polyethylene modified by exposure to Ar plasma for 1 min at 150 mtorr (PE-Ar), and PE-Ar after extensive reduction with 0.1 M diborane/THF for 24 hr (PE-Ar″). For each sample, an experimental C_{1s} spec-

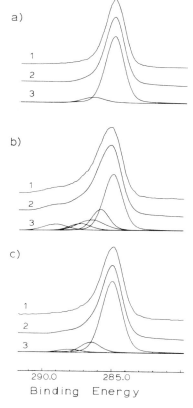

Figure 7. Reduced and oxidized polyethylene surfaces. The C_{1s} spectra of (a) control polyethylene; (b) Ar-plasma–oxidized polyethylene; and (c) Ar-plasma–oxidized polyethylene extensively reduced for 24 hr with diborane/THF. For each sample, 1 is the experimental spectrum; 2 is the curve fit, calculated spectrum; and 3 is the composite spectra used to generate 2.

290.0   285.0
Binding   Energy

trum (1), a calculated spectrum (2), and the composite spectra (3) are presented.

PE–H requires the inclusion of a low-intensity, high-binding-energy C_{1s} signal, interpreted to indicate residual surface oxidation. This oxidation probably exists as alcohol and/or carbonyl functions, although accurate determination is not possible. The C_{1s}/O_{1s} ratio for PE–H is 13, further supporting the presence of residual oxidation. In contrast, the ESCA spectra of PE–Ar has a C_{1s}/O_{1s} ratio of 1.8 and the C_{1s} spectrum indicates extensive surface oxidation. Beginning with the highest binding energy in the C_{1s} composite spectrum, the presence of

CO_2H, $\diagdown C=O$, $-\overset{|}{\underset{|}{C}}-OH$, α,β-unsaturated carbonyls/carboxylates, and CH_2 functionals is suggested, respectively.

The reduction of PE–Ar with BH_3/THF for 24 hr removes the highest binding energy, C_{1s} signal. This results from reduction of CO_2H functionals. Because esters are very slowly reduced,[64] the complete removal of the $-CO_2^-$ signal indicates that carboxylic esters were not generated with Ar plasma exposure of PE-H. The carbonyl C_{1s} area is attenuated, as expected for prolonged sample reduction. In addition, the peak at approximately 285.8 eV, assigned to conjugated olefins, is no longer required for a "good fit" of the experimental C_{1s} spectrum for PE-Ar". Collectively, these observations support the anticipated chemistry of diborane/THF reduction. Milder reduction of PE-Ar with diborane/THF for 3 hr produced an insignificant decrease in $\rangle C=O$ intensity but still removed the CO_2H and the conjugated $\rangle C=C\langle$ signals. It should be obvious that this curve fitting does not constitute a deconvolution and conclusions based on peak fitting are only speculative.

The results of chemical derivatization/ESCA analysis of PE-H, PE-Ar, and PE-Ar' (mildly reduced PE-Ar) are summarized in Table 8. Only the reaction of pentafluorophenylhydrazine incorporates fluorine in the control sample, supporting the earlier suggestion that residual carbonyls are present on PE-H. In contrast to PE-Ar, the mildly reduced sample shows an increase in surface hydroxyl concentration, a reduction in surface olefins, and no significant change

**TABLE 8.   Derivatization of Control Polyethylene (PE-H),
Polyethylene Oxidized by Exposure to Argon Plasma (PE-Ar),
and PE-Ar Mildly Reduced for 3 Hr with Diborane/THF (PE-Ar')**

Functional group	Derivative	C_{1s}/tag area ratio		
		PE-H	PE-Ar	PE-Ar'
$-OH$	$-O_2CCBr_3$	–	40	20
$-\overset{\|}{C}=O$	$C=NNHC_6F_5$	60	12	15
$-CO_2H$	$-CO_2CH_2CF_3$	–	7.7	–
$-\overset{\|}{C}=\overset{\|}{C}-$	$-\overset{\|}{C}-Hg(CF_3CO_2)$ $-\overset{\|}{C}-O-CH_2-CF_3$	–	1.4^a	14
$-CO_2H/-OH$	$-CO_2CH_2C_6F_5$ $-OCH_2C_6F_5$	–	3.6	38

$^a C_{1s}/Hg_{4f}$ area ratio.

in the amounts of carbonyls detected. No carboxylates are found on PE-Ar'. The reactions of PE-Ar and PE-Ar' with pentafluorobenzylbromide (PFBBr) introduce surface fluorine concentrations that differ by an order of magnitude. Because PFBBr reacts slowly with alcohols,[60] some derivatization of PE-Ar' with this reagent is expected. In contrast, the carboxylate salts of PE-Ar rapidly react with PFBBr, explaining the high F_{1s} area measured for PE-Ar treated with this reagent. Pentafluorobenzyl ethers will also be formed on PE-Ar.

The results shown in Table 8 are in good agreement with the expected chemistry resulting from mild BH_3/THF reduction and support the indicated selectivity of the derivatization reactions.

Similar procedures could be useful for evaluating the selectivity of other chemical derivatizations. $NaBH_4$ will reduce carbonyls in the presence of carboxylic acids.[65] Complementary studies with mild BH_3/THF reductions, extensive BH_3/THF reductions, and $NaBH_4$ reductions should prove helpful in further characterizing reaction selectivity. Reactions of a particular functional group with several different reagents could also be helpful in this respect.

5. SURFACE CHEMISTRY OF CHROMIC ACID AND CORONA-DISCHARGE-MODIFIED POLYPROPYLENE

Chemical derivatization/ESCA analysis offers a convenient method to compare the relative amounts of functional groups introduced with chromic acid and corona-discharge modification. The differences in modification mechanisms[41,66] could result in differences in the relative populations of various functional groups.

Table 9 contrasts the results of derivatizing chromic-acid(PP-ox)- and corona-discharge(PP-cd)-treated polypropylene with PFPH and trifluoroacetic anhydride.[67] The previous section verified the selectivity of the PFPH reaction with carbonyls. Trifluoroacetic anhydride (TFAA) is expected to react with any group which contains an active hydrogen. PP-H, PP-ox, and PP-cd do not show any F_{1s} or any N_{1s} ESCA intensity before derivatization.

Table 9 indicates that chemical oxidation and corona-discharge modification of polypropylene incorporate similar amounts of total surface oxygen. It is not likely that the concentration-depth profiles of oxidized groups in the two modified polymers are similar. As to the control polyethylene, residual surface carbonyls are present on PP-H, but no appreciable amount of surface functionals on PP-H react with TFAA (i.e., no measurable amount of surface alcohols and no surface carboxylic acids).

Carbonyls are the predominant oxygen containing functionals for both PP-ox and PP-cd. A large difference is measured in the relative surface alcohol/carboxylate concentration for each sample. PP-cd has a surface concentration of

TABLE 9. Derivatization of Polypropylene after Modification by Exposure to Chemical Oxidants or Corona Discharges

| Derivative | Area ratio | Sample | | |
		Control	Chromic acid	Corona discharge
—	C_{1s}/O_{1s}	52	5.5	6.2
╪—C=NNHC$_6$F$_5$	$C_{1s}/F_{1s}(\times 5)^a$	65	13.5	10.5
╪—CO$_2$COCF$_3$ ╪—O$_2$CCF$_3$	$C_{1s}/F_{1s}(\times 3)^a$	—	16.5	33.3

^{a}Multiplication by 5 (or 3) is required to correct for stoichiometry of PFPH (or TFAA) tag. The C_{1s}/F_{1s} ratios for the two derivatives can then be compared.

OH/CO$_2$H groups which is three times smaller than the concentration of surface carbonyls. For PP–ox, OH/CO$_2$H functionals are almost 13 times more dilute than carbonyl groups. While both modifications generate similar amounts of surface carbonyls, there are substantial differences in the amounts of OH/CO$_2$H groups generated. This interpretation is complicated by the possible presence of chromate ethers on PP–ox.[23,24] These inorganic ethers, if present, could prevent derivatization of surface alcohols. Briggs et al.[24] recently reported the presence of chromate ethers introduced via dichromate/H$_2$SO$_4$ oxidation. These ethers can be removed by treatment with nitric acid. This postoxidation procedure was not done in our preliminary study and could explain the low alcohol concentration measured for PP–ox.

6. FUNCTIONAL GROUP MOBILITY AND QUANTITATIVE ESCA ANALYSIS

Initial attempts to use derivatization/ESCA methods for semiquantitative analysis of polymer functional groups were frustrated on a number of occasions. Among these included an often drastic change in the relative surface nitrogen concentrations when PE–N was wet with a solvent.[68] This obviously complicated the solution derivatization and quantitation of surface nitrogen groups. Although the original C_{1s}/N_{1s} intensity ratio of nitrogen plasma modified polyethylene (PE–N) was 19 ± 2.6, much higher C_{1s}/N_{1s} intensity ratios were measured after mild exposure to isopropanol, diethyl ether, or acetonitrile. The level of nitrogen originally incorporated with plasma exposure was determined from 25 independent plasma-exposure-ESCA analysis experiments.

Early attempts to derivatize the amines of PE–N with pentafluorobenzaldehyde in acetonitrile were unsuccessful. ESCA analysis subsequent to the derivatization attempt revealed no F_{1s} and no N_{1s} intensities. As already discussed, the reaction of PE–N with pentafluorobenzaldehyde in pentane produced a surface showing an eminent F_{1s} ESCA signal. Furthermore, wetting the successfully derivatized surface with acetonitrile greatly attenuated the F_{1s} signal. These unexpected changes have important implications concerning the quantitative analysis of the surface amines.

Similar problems were encountered with the derivatization of oxygen-containing functions.[69] Attempts to react trimethylsilyl imidazole in acetonitrile with surface alcohols and surface carboxylic acids produced an increase in the C_{1s}/O_{1s} intensity ratio. No Si_{2p} intensity was detected. Other attempts in diethyl ether and pentane produced similar results. The formation of carboxylate salts with alcoholic NaOH or alcoholic Na_2CO_3 produced decreases in the C_{1s}/O_{1s} ratio. NaOH treatment also increased the relative intensity of the higher binding energy C_{1s} signal. A similar result has been reported by Burkstrand[31-33] for the vapor phase deposition of Cr, Ni, and Cu on polyvinyl alcohol and plasma-modified polystyrene. This author suggested the formation of a surface oxygen–metal complex and argued that this complex would accentuate high binding energy C_{1s} features. The increase in high-binding-energy carbon intensity implies a subsurface → surface migration of oxidized carbon functions.

Physically wetting PE–N is not required to reduce the relative surface nitrogen concentration. Exposing the nitrogen-plasma-modified sample to isopropanol vapor rapidly reproduces the decrease in nitrogen concentration achieved with isopropanol wetting. More importantly, slow decreases in relative N_{1s} intensity occur for samples aged in a vacuum dessicator. These observations are consistent with Burkstrand's[31-33] conclusions concerning the vapor phase deposition of Cr, Ni, and Cu on oxygen-containing polymers. Unusual changes in surface concentrations can occur without solvent assistance.

An obvious interpretation of these peculiar results is that low-molecular-weight nitrogen(or oxygen)-containing fragments are slowly removed from the polymer surface. Physical wetting or solvent vapor exposure increases the rate at which these fragments are removed. A similar argument was recently proposed by Briggs et al.[40] to explain changes in the ESCA spectra of corona-treated Mylar. For low-power plasma modification, the explanation of fragment removal is not supported by a number of important experimental observations. High-power corona discharges, however, could cause extensive fragmentation of surface polymer chains to produce the results reported for Mylar. The experimental evidence which refutes the extraction of low-molecular-weight fragments from PE–N is considered, and an alternative explanation is proposed.

As mentioned, wetting PE–N with isopropanol causes a large increase in the C/N atomic density ratio. We have found that certain conditions can restore the original C/N atomic density ratio and other conditions can often establish surface nitrogen concentrations that are almost three times larger than the concentration present just after plasma exposure. The increase in surface nitrogen would not be possible if nitrogen-containing groups were removed from the polymer. By way of illustration, let us consider Table 10. The C/N atomic density ratio of PE-N mildly wet with isopropanol increased about threefold of its value before solvent exposure. Wetting the sample with 0.1 M H_2SO_4 rapidly decreases the C/N density ratio to 12. An excess of sulfate is present until the sample is washed. The N_{1s} and S_{2p} binding energies indicate a surface ammonium sulfate. The protonated N_{1s} area is not effected by isopropanol washing; however, neutralization of the amine occurs rapidly and quantitatively with H_2O. The original

TABLE 10.   Mobility of Surface Amines:
Effects of Isopropanol Wetting and Protonation on the
Surface Amine Concentration

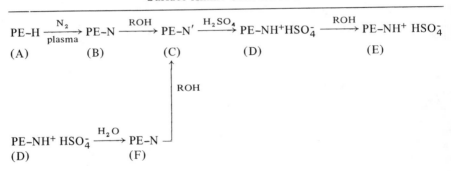

ESCA Data[a] for Above Reaction Sequence

Sample	C/N	N/S
A	—	—
B	31	—
C	97	—
D	12	0.6
E	16	1.4
F	40	—

[a]Atomic density ratios determined by multiplying the C_{1s}/N_{1s} (or N_{1s}/S_{2p}) ESCA intensity ratios by 1.62 (or 1.08).

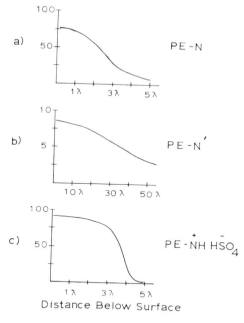

PE-N

PE-N'

PE-$\overset{+}{N}H$ HSO_4^-

Distance Below Surface

Figure 8. Mobility of surface functional groups. Generalized concentration-distance profiles for nitrogen plasma modified polyethylene (a) immediately after plasma exposure; (b) after mild wetting with isopropanol; and (c) after mild wetting with isopropanol followed by treatment with 0.1 M H_2SO_4. Abscissa normalized in units of mean free paths.

C/N ratio is restored. The free amine again responds to isopropanol wetting. This cycle can be repeated many times. Because the protonated amine salt is not removed from the polymer with solvent wetting, these groups must be covalently attached to the —CH_2— backbone. These results indicate that the amines are transported to and from the ESCA sampling depth as suggested in Figure 8. This functional group mobility has been interpreted as follows.[68]

Nitrogen plasma exposure incorporates a reproducible amount of surface amines on polyethylene. A sharp surface → subsurface concentration gradient of amines is established for PE-N immediately after plasma exposure. These surface amines are mobile and can migrate into the bulk polymer. Solvent exposure increases the rate of the dilution process. This mobility is not completely surprising because Fick's first law predicts a flux of surface groups into the bulk polymer to relax the large concentration gradient of surface groups. The dynamics of amorphous polymers are well substantiated,[70,71] and consequently migration of surface groups may be expected.

The result of this migration is to remove groups out of the ESCA sampling depth. When treated with H_2SO_4, subsurface amines are converted to protonated ammonium sulfates. Being insoluble in polyethylene, these protonated amines eventually reach a more stable position at the polymer surface.

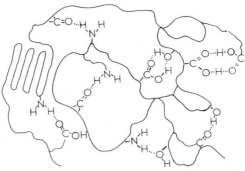

Figure 9. Surface cross-linking via intrastrand hydrogen bonding.

Many factors will influence the rate at which surface groups are diluted into the bulk. Recall that the surface of PE–N is highly oxidized and thus numerous intrastrand hydrogen bonds can exist. These hydrogen bonds can increase the surface cross-link density as suggested in Figure 9. These hydrogen bonds will retard chain mobility. Swelling solvents that can disrupt the intricate hydrogen-bond network promote increased mobility and are most effective in diluting surface groups into the bulk. The expected solvent dependence for the reduction of surface amines has been reported.[68]

We believe that functional group mobility is a general phenomena and likely occurs in many polymer surfaces. Functional group mobility would explain the time-dependent behavior that often plagues polymer applications. A germane observation is that solvent assistance is not required to change surface functionality. This mobility has been shown to seriously affect quantitative analysis of a modified polymer surface.[68] Appreciating this dynamic nature of a polymer surface, as revealed by ESCA analysis, should help broaden our understanding of the surface properties of a polymer.

7. CONCLUSIONS

1. Chemical derivatization can often enhance the detection of specific functional groups otherwise not resolvable with ESCA.

2. Functional groups on surface modified polymers possess a dynamic mobility; the surface concentration of these groups is strongly dependent on the surface–environment interface.

3. This mobility strongly influences the quantitative analysis of groups unique to a polymer surface.

REFERENCES

1. V. Trefiletti, G. Conio, B. Cavazza, F. Pioli, and E. Patrone, *Makromol. Chem., Rapid Commun.,* **1**, 351 (1980).

2. K. Kataoka, T. Tsuruta, T. Akaike, and Y. Sakurai, *Makromol. Chem.,* **181**, 1363 (1980).

3. B. Ratner, *Polymer Preprints,* **21**, 152 (1980). Papers presented at 179th American Chemical Society Meeting, Houston, Texas.

4. R. N. King, G. K. Iwamoto, J. D. Andrade, A. D. Haubold, and H. Shim, *Polymer Preprints,* **21**, 154 (1980). Papers presented at 179th American Chemical Society Meeting, Houston, Texas.

5. R. F. Gould, Ed., *Contact Angle, Wettability and Adhesion,* Advances in Chemistry Series No. 43, American Chemical Society, Washington, D.C., 1964.

6. N. J. Harrick, in *Internal Reflection Spectroscopy,* Wiley–Interscience, New York, 1967.

7. N. J. Harrick, in *Characterization of Metal and Polymer Surfaces,* Vol. 2, L. Lee, Ed., Academic Press, New York, 1977, pp. 153–192.

8. A. F. Orchard, in *Handbook of X-ray and Ultraviolet Photoelectron Spectroscopy,* D. Briggs, Ed., Heyden, London, 1977, Chap. 1.

9. C. S. Fadley, in *Electron Spectroscopy: Theory, Techniques, and Applications,* Vol. 2, C. R. Brundle and A. D. Baker, Eds., Academic Press, New York, 1978, Chap. 1.

10. W. Riggs and R. Swingle, *CRC Crit. Rev. Anal. Chem.,* **5**, 267, (1975).

11. A. W. Czanderna, Ed., *Methods of Surface Analysis,* Elsevier, New York, 1975.

12. M. P. Seah, *Surface Interface Anal.,* **1**, 86 (1979).

13. N. A. Alford, A. Barrie, I. W. Drummond, and P. C. Herd, *Surface Interface Anal.,* **1**, 36 (1979).

14. H. Werner, *Surface Interface Anal.,* **2**, 56 (1980).

15. N. R. Daly, Ed., *Advan. Mass Spectr.,* **7A**, 729–814 (1978).

16. P. N. Shott and B. O. Field, *Surface Interface Anal.,* **1**, 63 (1979).

17. J. A. Gardella and D. M. Hercules, *Anal. Chem.,* **52**, 226 (1980).

18. J. W. Rabalais, *Polymer Preprints,* **21**, 142 (1980). Papers presented at 179th American Chemical Society meeting, Houston, Texas.

19. R. Holm and S. Storp, *Surface Interface Anal.,* **2**, 96 (1980).

20. D. T. Clark, *Advan. Polymer Sci.,* **24**, 125 (1977).

21. D. T. Clark, in reference 8, Chap. 6.

22. D. T. Clark, in *Polymer Surfaces,* D. T. Clark and W. J. Feast, Eds., Wiley, New York, 1978, Chap. 16.

23. G. M. Whitesides, J. R. Rasmussen, and E. R. Stedronsky, *J. Amer. Chem. Soc.*, **99**, 4736 (1977).
24. D. Briggs, V. J. I. Zichy, D. M. Brewis, J. Comyn, R. H. Dalm, M. A. Green, and M. B. Konieczko, *Surface Interface Anal.*, **2**, 107 (1980).
25. K. Kato, *J. Appl. Polymer Sci.*, **18**, 3087 (1974).
26. J. V. Benham and T. J. Pullukat, *J. Appl. Polymer Sci.*, **20**, 3295 (1976).
27. D. R. Burfield and K. S. Law, *Polymer*, **20**, 620 (1979).
28. A. T. Bell and J. R. Hollahan, Eds., *Techniques and Applications of Plasma Chemistry*, Wiley, New York, 1974.
29. D. T. Clark and A. J. Dilks, *J. Polymer Sci. Polymer Chem. Ed.*, **15**, 2321 (1977).
30. R. W. Murray, *Acc. Chem. Res.*, **13**, 135 (1980).
31. J. M. Burkstrand, *Appl. Phys. Lett.*, **33**, 387 (1978).
32. J. M. Burkstrand, *J. Vacuum Sci. Technol.*, **16**, 363 (1979).
33. J. M. Burkstrand, *J. Vacuum Sci. Technol.*, **16**, 1072 (1979).
34. S. Yamakawa, *Macromolecules*, **12**, 1222 (1979).
35. W. Riggs, *Anal. Chem.*, **47**, 1837 (1975).
36. D. M. Wyatt, R. C. Gray, J. C. Carver, D. M. Hercules, and L. W. Masters, *Appl. Spectr.*, **28**, 439 (1974).
37. D. Briggs, *J. Mater. Sci.*, **12**, 429 (1977).
38. D. Briggs and C. R. Kendall, *Polymer*, **20**, 1053 (1979).
39. H. Yasuda, H. C. Marsh, E. S. Brandt, and C. N. Reilley, *J. Polymer Sci. Polymer Chem. Ed.*, **15**, 991 (1977).
40. D. Briggs, D. G. Rance, C. R. Kendall, and A. R. Blythe, *Polymer*, **21**, 895 (1980).
41. G. C. S. Collins, A. C. Lowe, and D. Nicholas, *European Polymer J.*, **9**, 1173 (1973).
42. C. D. Wagner, W. M. Riggs, L. E. Davis, and J. F. Moulder and G. E. Muilenberg, *Handbook of X-ray Photoelectron Spectroscopy*, Perkin-Elmer Corporation, Physical Electronics Division, Eden Prairie, Minn., 1979.
43. D. T. Clark, A. Dilks, and H. R. Thomas, *J. Polymer Sci. Polymer Chem. Ed.*, **16**, 1461 (1978).
44. S. Evans, in reference 8, Chap. 3.
45. R. S. Williams, D. Denley, D. A. Shirley, and J. Stohr, *J. Amer. Chem. Soc.*, **102**, 5717 (1980).
46. D. T. Clark, W. J. Feast, W. K. R. Musgrave, and I. Ritchie, *J. Polymer Sci. Polymer Chem. Ed.*, **13**, 857 (1975).
47. P. Cadman, J. D. Scott, and J. M. Thomas, *Surface Interface Anal.*, **1**, 115 (1979).
48. D. Briggs, in reference 8, Chap. 4, pp. 171–173.
49. C. D. Wagner, in reference 8, Chap. 7.

50. C. D. Wagner, *Faraday Discussions Chem. Soc.*, **60**, 291 (1975).
51. C. D. Wagner, L. H. Gale, and R. H. Raymond, *Anal. Chem.*, **51**, 466 (1979).
52. C. D. Wagner, D. A. Zatko, and R. H. Raymond, *Anal. Chem.*, **52**, 1445 (1980).
53. D. S. Everhart and C. N. Reilley, *Anal. Chem.*, **53**, 665 (1981).
54. W. Riggs, and D. J. Dwight, *J. Electron Spectr.*, **5**, 447 (1974).
55. J. S. Hammond, *Abstr. Amer. Chem. Soc. Nat. Meeting, Div. Polymer Chem., Houston*, **179** (1980).
56. C. D. Batich and R. W. Wendt, *Abstr. Amer. Chem. Soc. Nat. Meeting, Div. Polymer Chem., Houston*, **179** (1980).
57. C. D. Batich and R. W., Wendt, private communication, Northeast ESCA Users' Group Meeting XVIII, Hercules Inc., Wilmington, Del., 1980.
58. D. Williams, private communication, Northeast ESCA Users' Group Meeting XVI, RCA, Princeton, N.J., May, 1979.
59. M. Millard and M. Marsi, *Anal. Chem.*, **46**, 1820 (1974).
60. K. Blau and G. S. King, Eds., *Handbook of Derivatives for Chromatography*, Heyden, London, 1977.
61. G. I. Likhtenshtein, *Spin Labeling Methods in Molecular Biology*, Wiley, New York, 1976.
62. W. G. Miller, in *Spin Labeling, Vol. II: Theory and Applications*, L. J. Berliner, Ed., Academic Press, New York, 1979, Chap. 4.
63. D. M. Ullevig and J. F. Evans, *Anal. Chem.*, **52**, 1467 (1980).
64. H. Brown, P. Heim, and N. M. Yoon, *J. Amer. Chem. Soc.*, **92**, 1637 (1970).
65. L. Fieser and M. Fieser, *Reagents for Organic Synthesis*, Vol. 1, Wiley, New York, 1967.
66. P. Blais, D. J. Carlsson, G. W. Csullog, and D. M. Wiles, *J. Colloid Inter. Sci.*, **47**, 636 (1974).
67. F. F. -L. Ho and E. G. Gregory, unpublished results.
68. D. S. Everhart and C. N. Reilley, *Surface Interface Anal.*, **3**, 126 (1981).
69. D. S. Everhart and C. N. Reilley, unpublished results.
70. L. Rebenfeld, D. J. Makarewics, H. D. Weigman, and G. L. Wilkes, *Macromol. Sci.–Rev. Macromol. Chem.*, **C15**, 279 (1976).
71. J. Schaefer, E. O. Strejskal, and R. Buchdahl, *Macromolecules*, **10**, 385 (1977).

CHARACTERIZATION OF POLYMER-ANCHORED HOMOGENEOUS CATALYSTS: AN ESCA APPLICATION*

FLOYD F.-L. HO

*Hercules Incorporated
Research Center
Wilmington, Delaware*

In the past few years, we have witnessed an intense interest and a rapid development in the use of functionalized polymer as support for catalysts. A number of review articles, chapters, and monographs have appeared recently in the literature.[1-11] As with the more conventional metal oxide supported catalysts, the polymer-anchored species also offer the ease of separation, have less corrosion, and are free from solubility limitations—all important considerations in industrial applications. It has been further demonstrated that homogeneous catalyst anchored on selected polymer exhibits enhanced activity and stability. The tendency toward deactivation in soluble homogeneous catalysis through bimolecular reaction in forming an inactive dimer can be prevented in this case. However, the popularity of polymer as support for catalysts probably arises from the wide selection of polymers available and from the existence of heterogeneous processes for functioning the polymer surface. These advantages have been utilized for the synthesis of catalysts with multiple sites to achieve simultaneous catalytic reactions. Examples of asymmetric catalysis by a supported chiral complex have been reported. The possibility of a design of catalyst for a specific investigation is certainly attractive.

In this chapter, we shall review the application of ESCA for the characterization of polymer-anchored homogeneous catalysts, from the literature as well as from our own experience. This contribution will explore a subject area bridging that of the previous chapter on polymer surfaces by Reilley, Everhart, and Ho and that of the following chapter on heterogeneous catalysts by Hercules, and Klein.

Even though the catalytic reaction of a polymer-anchored catalyst is truly a surface phenomenon, where a surface-sensitive and specific technique like ESCA

---

*Hercules Research Center Contribution No. 1745

should enjoy a wide acceptance, applications of ESCA in this area has just begun. By far, the analytical techniques used most often in the characterization of such catalyst are still elemental analysis and infrared spectroscopy.

To explore the enormous potential of ESCA in this area of research, let us begin by examining one of the more popular schemes of synthesis of the polymer-anchored catalysts:

In this sequence of reactions, each step including the chloromethylation, phosphination, and catalyst anchoring provides a unique opportunity for ESCA application. Each reaction is heterogeneous in nature, involving chemical processes taking place at the polymer surface, and each step involves reaction of an element sensitive and specific for ESCA characterization. For example, the chloromethylation of polystyrene can be followed by measurement of the Cl_{2p} signal, while the phosphination process can be traced from the changes of either Cl_{2p} or P_{2p} signals. Likewise, the anchoring of metal ions can also be studied by ESCA.

A portion of ESCA spectra showing the phosphination process is shown in Figure 1. The phosphination of chloromethylated polystyrene in this case was carried out in refluxing tetrahydrofuran for 12 hr with excess lithiumdiphenylphosphine. The degree of phosphination of the chloromethyl groups was shown to be 100%. The doublet appearance of the P_{2p} signal in Figure 1b arises from the overlap of the $P_{2p_{1/2}}$ and $P_{2p_{3/2}}$, with the smaller signal at higher binding energy belonging to $P_{2p_{1/2}}$. The fact that there are only two signals separated by approximately 1 eV indicates the existence of phosphorus mainly in one oxidation state. A $P_{2p_{3/2}}$ at 130.7 eV compares with 130.3 eV reported for triphenylphosphine.[12] Triphenylphosphine oxide should be at ~132.4 eV. After careful washing, the material was shown to be very stable. Exposure to air and sunlight for 2 weeks did not appreciably affect either the ESCA signal or the characteristics of the support. Furthermore, the thoroughly crushed samples have similar ESCA spectra, indicating a rather homogeneous distribution of the functional group throughout the microsphere on the polymer surface.

Two examples of partially phosphinated chloromethyl substituted polystyrene are shown in Figure 2. The ratio of the integrated signal areas from P_{2p} to Cl_{2p}, corrected for the difference in signal sensitivity, is 4 to 1 in Figure 2a and 1 to 1 in Figure 1b. Therefore, these two samples shown in Figures 2a and 2b are

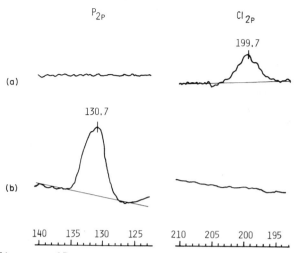

Figure 1. ESCA spectra of P_{2p} and Cl_{2p} of a chloromethylated polystyrene support before (*a*) and after (*b*) phosphination.

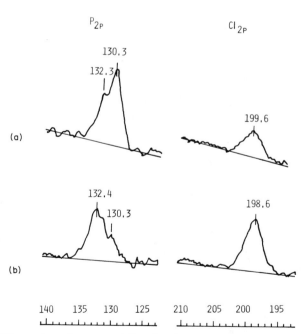

Figure 2. ESCA spectra of two partially phosphinated chloromethyl substituted polystyrene: 80% (*a*) and 50% (*b*) phosphination.

approximately 80% and 50% phosphinated. This is a simple and direct application of ESCA. However, a closer examination of Figures 1 and 2 reveals some subtle but significant differences, which illustrate further the application of ESCA. For example, the major P_{2p} peak in Figure 2b is at a higher binding energy at 132.4 eV and the Cl_{2p} is centered at a lower binding energy at 198.6 eV. This observation seems to lend experimental support for a structure put forth previously by Mitchell and Whitehurst[13] that involves the quaternization of the newly introduced phosphine group by the unreacted chloromethyl group:

The phosphonium cation will move the P_{2p} to a higher binding energy, while the Cl^- anion will make the Cl_{2p} appear at a lower binding energy (198.6 versus 199.6 eV). The probability of forming such a quaternary ion will of course be less for the sample shown in Figure 2a, where there is already a high 80% phosphination. The chance becomes practically zero for a sample with a 100% reaction (see Figure 1b). This quaternized structure is consistent with the observation that this support makes a less active catalyst. Whitehurst[5] reported a similar effect.

ESCA has also been used by Tang et al.[14] to assist in characterizing a support made from a commercial ion exchange resin, such as Rohm and Haas's XN1010, and a bifunctional phosphine, such as tris(4-dimethylaminophenyl)phosphine. It is necessary in this case to know whether the ionic linkage between the sulfonic acid of the resin and the bifunctional phosphine is with the nitrogen or with the phosphorus end of the ligand. ESCA data cited in Table 1 demonstrate that the protonation, as well as the quaternization by methyl bromide, occurs at the phosphorus. The P atom was found ionic and N mainly covalent. Upon further conversion to a catalyst, the investigators[14] were able to show from

TABLE 1.   ESCA Data[a] of Polymeric Supports

Polymer	P_{2p}	N_{1s}
(P) —⟨benzene⟩— $CH_2P\phi_2$	130.7	—
$P\phi_3$	130.4	—
XN1010H/ ($>$N —⟨benzene⟩—)$_3$ P[b]	132.2	399.4
($>$N —⟨benzene⟩—)$_3$ P[b]	130.0	399.3
XN1010Na/ ($>$N —⟨benzene⟩—)$_3$ PMe^+Br^- [b]	132.4	399.6
($>$N —⟨benzene⟩—)$_3$ PMe^+Br^- [b]	132.0	399.2

[a] Binding energies in electron volts with reference to C_{1s} at 285.0 eV.
[b] From reference 14.

ESCA data that the metal Pt and Co bond covalently with the free pendant amino group of the ligand.

The anchoring of metal ions onto the functionalized polymer surface can be accomplished in a number of ways, such as a simple ligand exchange or a "bridge splitting" of a dimeric complex. Each process has a different efficiency, which can be effectively investigated by ESCA. Some examples of our work are shown in Table 2. Catalyst C1 was prepared by bridge splitting a chloronorbornadiene rhodium(I) dimer in refluxing hexane for 24 hr, followed by additional refluxing in tetrahydrofuran (THF). The reaction for C2 took only about 10 min at room temperature. Catalysts C3 and C4, involving ligand exchanges of the triphenylphosphine group and the phosphinated polymer support, had much slower reaction times.

An ESCA spectrum of catalyst C1 is shown in Figure 3, and a summary of ESCA data of C1 to C4 is given in Table 3. The atomic ratio of P/Cl/Rh for C1 is approximately 2:2:1, indicating the presence of $(-CH_2P\phi_2)_2Rh(C1)_2$. Furthermore, electron spin resonance (ESR) spectra of this sample showed paramagnetic Rh(II) signals. There were a total of five lines on the spectrum. The majority of Rh(II) has an axial symmetry with $g_\parallel = 2.004$ and $g_\perp = 2.040$. The minor one has

TABLE 2. Efficiency of Rh Attachment on a Phosphinated Polymer Support

Catalyst		Reaction time
C1	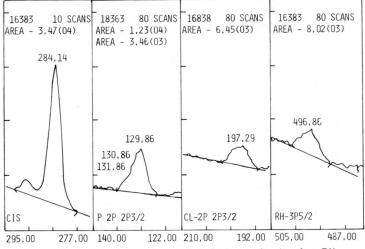	Reflux 24 hr
C2		10 min at room temperature
C3		Several weeks
C4		Several weeks

CATALYST C1

16383 10 SCANS	18363 80 SCANS	16838 80 SCANS	16383 80 SCANS
AREA - 3.47(04)	AREA - 1.23(04)	AREA - 6.45(03)	AREA - 8.02(03)
	AREA - 3.46(03)		

284.14

130.86
131.86   129.86

197.29

496.86

CIS

P 2P 2P3/2

CL-2P 2P3/2

RH-3P5/2

295.00   277.00 140.00   122.00 210.00   192.00 505.00   487.00

Figure 3. ESCA spectra of an anchored Rh complex (catalyst C1).

140

TABLE 3. Summary of ESCA Data

Element	C_{1s}	O_{1s}	P_{2p}	Cl_{2p}	$Rh_{3p\,3/2}$	
Binding energy	285.0	533.97	130.69	198.12	497.69	C1
Atomic %	78.53	19.54	0.78	0.77	0.38	
Binding energy	285.0	533.43	130.72	198.86	497.68	C2
Atomic %	73.34	22.57	1.89	1.52	0.68	
Binding energy	285.0	533.16	131.57	198.29	498.15	C3
Atomic %	87.77	8.85	2.54	0.69	0.27	
Binding energy	285.0	532.96	130.82	197.96	496.67	C4
Atomic %	92.38	5.85	0.99	0.60	0.18	

a orthorhombic symmetry with $g_1 = 2.017$, $g_2 = 2.031$, and $g_3 = 1.970$. Based on the ESCA and ESR data, catalyst C1 was proposed to have the following structure:

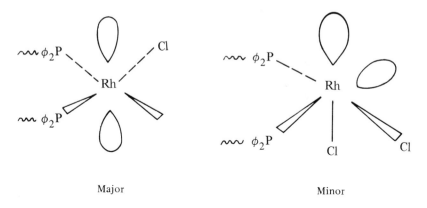

Major   Minor

Catalyst C1 was synthesized from a 100% phosphinated support (Figure 1b), while C2 to C4 were from a partially phosphinated support (Figure 2). The interpretation of the ESCA data in the C2 to C4 cases is somewhat more difficult since there are also contributions to the P and Cl signals from the unreacted support. The lower amount of incorporation of Rh in these cases, relative to the amount of P, may also be an effect of the formation of the quaternary P structure indicated earlier.

These catalysts were tested in our laboratory[15] to determine their activities and selectivities in the hydrogenation of a diene, 5-methylene-2-norbornene (I).

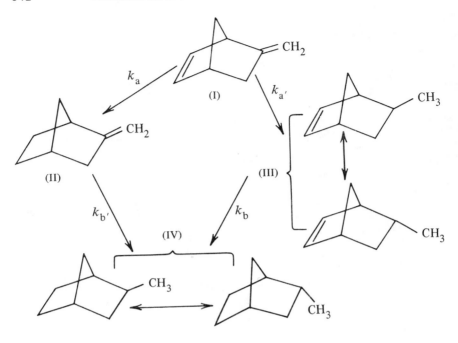

Most of these catalysts were found to have some activity in the hydrogenation of (I). They are also more selective in hydrogenating the norbornene double bond, since compound (II) is the major product detected.

ESCA data of polymer-supported Rh catalyst and several related compounds have been reported by Imanaka et al.[16,17] and are presented in Table 4. The catalysts were found extremely stable, showing no change in ESCA spectra after use in olefin hydrogenation. Also, no change on either ESCA, ESR, or IR was observed after the catalysts had been exposed to air for several months.

On a similarly chloromethylated and phosphinated polystyrene polymer, Pd(II)[18] and Pd(0)[19] have been anchored. ESCA data of these complexes are shown in Table 5. Both the divalent and the zerovalent catalysts were found to be very stable, with no observable change after use or after exposure to air and moisture. The reduction of Ⓟ—PdCl$_2$ to Ⓟ—Pd(0)Pϕ_3 by hydrazine hydrate in the presence of triphenylphosphine was followed by ESCA. The activity is comparable to that of the analogous homogeneous catalysts and does not change after initial usage.

Aminated polystyrenes have been employed to anchor a Pd(II) complex.[20] The ESCA data are given in Table 6. The Pd$_{3d}$ binding energies for all these polymer-supported complexes were almost constant and independent of the metal loading. Furthermore, the peak intensity ratios of Cl$_{2p}$/Pd$_{3d}$ and N$_{1s}$/Pd$_{3d}$

TABLE 4.   ESCA Data[a] of Polymer Supported Rh Catalyst

Catalyst	$Rh_{3d_{3/2}}$		$Rh_{3d_{5/2}}$		Cl_{2p}		P_{2p}
(P)—RhCl$_2$[b] (fresh)	313.7		309.1		199.2		—
(P)—RhCl$_2$[b] (recycled)	313.7		309.1		199.2		—
	(b)	(c)	(b)	(c)	(b)	(c)	(c)
Rh Metal	311.8	312.1	307.1	307.2	—	—	—
$(\phi_3P)_3$RhCl	312.7	312.5	308.2	307.2	199.5	198.2	131.7
$(\phi_3P)_2$Rh(CO)Cl	313.2	313.6	308.4	309.0	198.7	198.7	131.7
H$(\phi_3P)_2$Rh(CO)	312.9	313.5	308.1	108.7	—	—	131.5
RhCl$_3$	314.4	315.0	309.7	310.3	199.5	199.5	—

[a] Binding energies in electron volts with reference to C_{1s} at 285.0 eV.
[b] From reference 16.
[c] From reference 17.

TABLE 5.   ESCA Data[a] of Pd Supported on Phosphinated Polystyrene

	$Pd_{3d_{3/2}}$	$Pd_{3d_{5/2}}$	P_{2p}	Cl_{2p}
(P)—PdCl$_2$[b]	344.0	338.6	—	199.1
(P)—PdCl$_2$[b] (recycled)	343.8	338.5	—	199.2
(P)—PdCl$_2$[c]	344.0	338.6	132.0	—
(P)—Pd—Pϕ_3[c]	342.6	337.6	132.3	—
PdCl$_2$(Pϕ_3)$_2$[b]	343.6	338.3	132.0	—
PdCl$_2$[b,c]	343.6	338.1	—	199.3
Pd(Pϕ_3)$_4$[c]	341.4	336.2	131.2	—

[a] Binding energies in electron volts with reference to C_{1s} at 285.0 eV.
[b] From reference 18.
[c] From reference 19.

were also constant and independent of the metal loading. These data show that a Pd species having the same composition is formed on the polymer surface regardless of the degree of metal loading.

In another study, Salaneck et al.[21] concluded from the ESCA data that the surface functional group of the ion exchange resin adopts a preferred orientation with the —SO$_3^-$ K$^+$ dipoles pointing mostly away from the surface.

It is hoped that this brief discussion, drawn from the literature as well as from our own data, serves to illustrate the potential usefulness of ESCA in this area of

TABLE 6. ESCA Data[a] of Pd Supported on Aminated Polystyrene[b]

Polymer[c]	Pd/N	$Pd_{3d_{3/2}}$	$Pd_{3d_{5/2}}$	Cl_{2p}	N_{1s}
(1)	0.3	343.8	338.5	199.4	402.0
(1)	0.4	343.8	338.4	199.3	401.8
(1)	0.5	343.7	338.4	199.2	401.9
(1)	0.7	343.6	338.4	199.4	402.1
(1)	1.0	343.7	338.3	199.2	401.9
(2)	0.3	343.5	338.2	199.2	401.7
(2)	0.5	343.6	338.2	199.1	401.4
(2)	0.7	343.6	338.3	199.3	401.8
(2)	1.0	343.5	338.1	199.1	401.8

[a] Binding energies in eV with reference to C_{1s} at 285.0 eV.
[b] Reference (20).
[c] Polymer (1) = poly-4-dimethylaminomethylstyrene.
Polymer (2) = poly-4-pyrrolidinomethylstyrene.

research involving polymer-supported catalysts. Because of the particular surface sensitivity of ESCA and because of its ability to provide chemical information (such as the oxidation state, chemical bonding, and molecular orientation), ESCA should be of unique importance in the characterization of these popular catalysts. Although publication of ESCA papers on this subject is still rare, it has had a good beginning.

ACKNOWLEDGMENTS

The author is indebted to Prof. B. C. Gates for advice and encouragement, to Mr. C. L. Bodolus for experimental assistance, and to Hercules Incorporated for permission to publish this paper.

REFERENCES

1. J. C. Bailar, Jr., *Catalysis Rev.–Sci. Eng.,* **10**, 17 (1974).

2. R. H. Grubbs, E. M. Sweet, and S. Phisanbut, in *Catalysis in Organic Synthesis,* P. N. Rylander and H. Greenfield, Ed., Academic Press, New York, 1976.

3. Y. Chauvin, D. Commereuc, and F. Dawans, *Progr. Polymer Sci.,* **5**, 95 (1977).

4. B. C. Gates, in *Chemistry and Chemical Engineering of Catalytic Processes,* R. Prins and G. C. A. Schuit, Ed., Sijthoff & Noordhoff, Germantown, Maryland, 1980.

5. D. D. Whitehurst, *CHEMTECH,* **10,** 44 (1980).

6. D. C. Sherrington, in *Polymer-Supported Reactions in Organic Synthesis,* P. Hodge and D. C. Sherrington, Eds., Wiley, New York, 1980.

7. C. U. Pittman, Jr., in *Polymer-Supported Reactions in Organic Synthesis,* P. Hodge and D. C. Sherrington, Eds., Wiley, New York, 1980.

8. M. A. Kraus and A. Patchornik, *J. Polymer Sci. Macromol. Rev.,* **15,** 55 (1980).

9. N. K. Mathur, C. K. Narang, and R. E. Williams, *Polymers as Aids in Organic Chemistry,* Academic Press, New York, 1980.

10. C. H. Brubaker, Jr., in *Catalysis in Organic Synthesis,* G. V. Smith, Ed., Academic Press, New York, 1977.

11. J. M. Basset and A. K. Smith, in *Fundamental Research in Homogeneous Catalysis,* M. Tsutsui and R. Ugo, Ed., Plenum Press, New York, 1977.

12. C. D. Wagner, W. M. Riggs, L. E. Davis, J. F. Moulder, and G. E. Muilenberg, *Handbook of X-ray Photoelectron Spectroscopy,* Perkin-Elmer Corporation, Physical Electronics Division, Eden Prairie, Minn., 1979.

13. T. O. Mitchell and D. D. Whitehurst, paper presented at the Third North American Conference of the Catalysis Society, San Francisco, February 1974.

14. S. C. Tang, T. E. Paxson, and L. Kim, *J. Mol. Catalysis,* **9,** 313 (1980).

15. F. F.-L. Ho, C. L. Bodolus, and B. C. Gates, paper in preparation for publication; preliminary results reported by C. L. Bodolus in a Senior Thesis, Department of Chemical Engineering, University of Delaware, 1979.

16. T. Imanaka, K. Kaneda, S. Teranishi, and M. Terasawa, *Proceedings of the 6th International Congress on Catalysis, London,* A-41, 509 (1977).

17. Y. Okamoto, N. Ishida, T. Imanaka, and S. Teranishi, *J. Catalysis,* **58,** 82 (1979).

18. M. Terasawa, K. Kaneda, T. Imanaka, and S. Teranishi, *J. Catalysis,* **51,** 406 (1978).

19. M. Terasawa, K. Kaneda, T. Imanaka, and S. Teranishi, *J. Organometallic Chem.,* **162,** 403 (1978).

20. M. Terawawa, K. Sano, K. Kaneda, T. Imanaka, and S. Teranishi, *Chem. Commun.,* p. 650 (1978).

21. W. R. Salaneck, H. W. Gibson, F. C. Bailey, J. M. Pochan, and H. R. Thomas, *J. Polymer Sci., Polymer Lett. Ed.,* **16,** 447 (1978).

ELECTRON SPECTROSCOPY
FOR CHEMICAL ANALYSIS
APPLIED TO
HETEROGENEOUS CATALYSIS

DAVID M. HERCULES and JOSEPH C. KLEIN

Department of Chemistry
University of Pittsburgh
Pittsburgh, Pennsylvania

1. INTRODUCTION

Research of heterogeneous catalysis has been an extremely active area of science for more than half a century. The understanding of heterogeneous catalysis is not only important scientifically but has both practical and economic implications. For example, catalysts are used to reform crude oil, to produce polymers, and to convert coal into liquid fuels. To facilitate catalytic research, analytical instrumentation has been developed which has the ability to analyze the surfaces of materials. X-ray photoelectron spectroscopy (XPS), which has also been given the name electron spectroscopy for chemical analysis (ESCA), is one of these surface-analytical tools.

The authors would like to indicate that the content that follows is a brief review of how ESCA has been applied to heterogeneous catalysis. However, this is not an exhaustive review of the subject by any means. The content will heavily stress a review of the work performed in our laboratory, with some discussion of related work by others. The intent of this work is to allow the reader to obtain an elementary understanding of how ESCA is being applied to catalysis systems. This work is a result of a talk given at the seventh annual meeting of the Federation of Analytical Chemistry and Spectroscopy Societies (FACSS).

ESCA has recently (over the past decade) become a common tool for heterogeneous catalysis research. As ESCA has matured, its use for characterizing catalyst systems has increased. In the early 1970s only a few papers appeared on the application of ESCA to catalysts. However, at the beginning of the 1980s, ESCA applied to heterogeneous catalysis has become almost commonplace. The $Co/Mo/Al_2O_3$ hydrodesulfurization catalysts (HDS) and related systems, for example, have been analyzed most extensively by ESCA. However, applications to other catalytic systems are increasing.

The intent of this review is to examine the application of ESCA to heterogeneous catalysts. The types of information ESCA can provide, its advantage and disadvantages will be discussed with reference to complementary techniques that have been applied to catalysis. ESCA can provide both qualitative and quantitative information about the chemical nature of surfaces.[1-3] Because of its inherent surface sensitivity, ESCA is extremely useful for studying surface phenomena such as adsorption, oxidation and catalysis. In addition to its surface sensitivity, ESCA is also chemical specific. Therefore, ESCA does not only indicate the surface elemental composition but can provide information about the chemical states of the elements detected through analysis of chemical shifts. Not only can chemical information be derived from ESCA, but some physical characteristics such as particle size can be correlated with ESCA measurements.[4-6]

Heterogeneous catalysts basically fall into two categories, supported and unsupported. Both types of catalysts generally employ small particles to obtain very large surface areas (ca. 100–200 m^2/g). Supported catalysts use a high surface area "supposedly" inert support (i.e., Al_2O_3 or SiO_2) to disperse a catalytically active material. The unsupported catalyst systems usually consist of finely divided pure material, although in many cases both supported and unsupported catalysts use more than one active component, that is, a promoter has been added. In $Co/Mo/Al_2O_3$ catalysts, the Co is considered to be the promoter of the Mo/Al_2O_3 catalyst system. Similarly, mixed supports ($Al_2O_3 \cdot SiO_2$) may be used.

Supported catalysts are generally prepared in a two-step process. First, the catalytic material must be applied to the support. Salts of catalytic materials such as $Ni(NO_3)_2$, $Co(NO_3)_2$, and NH_4ReO_4 are dissolved in water. The solution is then poured over the support and the catalysts is dried and calcined (i.e., heated) to remove the unwanted ions such as NO_3^- or NH_4^+. This method of preparation is usually referred to as *impregnation.* However, when only enough solution is used to just fill the pores of the support, the method is called *impregnation to incipient wetness.* Many times the solubility of the salts used is not sufficient to employ impregnation to incipient wetness for preparing supported catalysts.

Supported catalysts can also be prepared by coprecipitation. Coprecipitation is performed by dissolving salts of the support and catalyst in the same solution. Then, by altering the pH of the solution, the two components will precipitate simultaneously. The precipitate is washed, dried, and calcined to remove unwanted ions and water.

Supported catalysts are usually chemically treated at the second step after drying and calcining to activate them. Many of the catalysts are active in the metallic form; therefore, the calcined catalysts are usually reduced with hydrogen. Other methods of activation are employed depending on the use or the type of catalyst. The Mo HDS catalyst is a case where no further treatment is needed after calcination. The oxidic catalyst is converted to the active catalyst during the hydrodesulfurization reaction, although presulfiding is common.

Unsupported catalysts have about as many methods of preparations as there are types of unsupported catalysts. For example, cracking catalysts such as Zeolites require no elaborate preparation before use. However, alumina–silica gel cracking catalysts are not just a mixture of Al_2O_3/SiO_2, but are prepared by incorporation of the Al_2O_3 into the SiO_2. Alloy catalysts are usually prepared by alloying metals, which are then powdered for easy use. Raney catalysts are unsupported catalysts that employ an alloy of catalytic metal and aluminum. The alloy is treated with strong base to remove the Al, which produces a high-surface-area metallic catalyst.

Because of the variety of unsupported catalysts, the authors decided to briefly discuss two specific topics which they are familiar with. Many general references exist in the literature that present the basic concepts, types, processes, preparation, and general overviews of catalysis.[7-10]

2. ESCA INFORMATION AND CAPABILITIES

2.1. Surface Sensitivity

One aspect of ESCA that makes the technique especially applicable to heterogeneous catalysis is its inherent surface sensitivity. The mean free paths (MFP) of the photoejected electron determine the sampling depth of the ESCA experiment.[11] The exciting x-rays penetrate a sample of a few micrometers. Although,

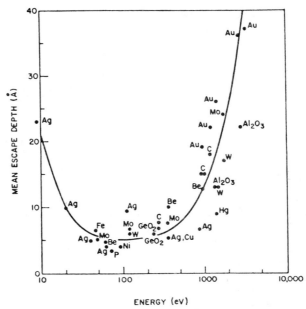

Figure 1.   Mean free path of electrons in solids. (After Riviere.[12])

the MFP of a ~ 1 keV electron is about 15 Å, this corresponds to about 95% of the photoejected electrons originating from the top 45 Å of the sample.

The MFP of a photoejected electron is a function of both the kinetic energy of the ejected electron and the sample matrix.[11] The MFP plotted as a function of electron kinetic energy is represented in Figure 1. Since the escape depth varies considerably over the range of kinetic energies associated with ESCA, it is very important to consider sampling depth when quantitating signals from catalysts, especially if the kinetic energies of the photoelectron lines are quite different (ca. 500 eV).

The nature of the sample matrix from which the ejected electron is emitted affects the escape depth. As the electron is being ejected, a number of interaction processes can take place to cause energy loss that can be attributed to matrix effects.[12] Some of the matrix effects are inelastic scattering from neighboring atoms, plasmon interaction, and phonon interaction in a solid.[13,14] These matrix effects depend on the chemical nature of the sample. For example, Cu metal has a greater probability of having plasmon interaction than its respective oxides because it is a conductor.[15] Therefore, escape depths are usually greater for oxides than for metals.[15] Hence, when attempting quantitative measurements, the matrix should be considered especially when mixed matrices are present such as a conductor on an insulator (i.e., Ni metal supported on Al_2O_3 or SiO_2). This is especially true for supported systems where the support properties affect the intensity ratios. Brinen et al. indicated support effects on quantitation for Rh supported on carbon and alumina.[16]

2.2. Quantitation

One of the most important features of ESCA applied to catalysis is the ability to quantitatively analyze surfaces. The number of emitted electrons is a function of the number of atoms on the surface. However, the measured signal depends on many factors. Equation 1 describes the intensity of the ESCA signal originating from the surface layers:

$$I_i = FSN_i\sigma_i\lambda_iT_i \, (1 - e^{-d/\lambda_i})$$ (1)

where I_i = intensity of i photoelectron of a given energy
  F = x-ray photon flux
  S = fraction of electrons detected by spectrometer
  N_i = number of atoms per cubic centimeter emitting i photoelectrons
  σ_i = atomic cross sections of i-level ionization
  λ_i = mean free path of ith electron
  T_i = transmission factors of i photoelectrons through a surface layer of contaminants
  d = sample thickness

In order to obtain absolute quantitation, all the parameters must be known accurately. This has not been accomplished because of difficulties involved in evaluating the parameters. In the past, workers have either used calibration standards or have measured empirical sensitivity factors to obtain relative concentrations of the surface species.[17,18]

Kerkhof and Moulijn[19] have proposed a quantitative model that would allow ESCA intensities to be used to quantitate the surface species on supported catalysts. The model is applied to high-surface-area supports with monolayer coverage. One can predict the ESCA intensity ratio of promoter/support by knowing the bulk ratio of promoter/support and their respective photoelectron cross sections. The model describes a catalyst as sheets of support of thickness t and a promoter of cubic crystallites with wall dimension c. The model is visually shown in Figure 2. The derived intensity ratio of the promoter p to the support s is described by the following equation:

$$\left(\frac{I_p}{I_s}\right)_{exptl} = \left(\frac{p}{s}\right)_b \frac{D_{ep}\sigma_p\beta_1(1 - e^{-\alpha_1})(1 + e^{-\beta_2})}{D_{es}\sigma_s 2\alpha_1(1 - e^{\beta_2})}$$ (2)

where $(p/s)_b$ = bulk atomic % of the promoter and support

$D_{(\epsilon)}$ = detection efficiency (ϵ - kinetic energy of electron)

σ_x = photoelectron cross section of x

$\beta_1 = t/\lambda_{ss}$ (t is sheet thickness; λ_{ss} escape depth of support)

$\alpha_1 = c/\lambda_{pp}$ (c is crystallite size; λ_{pp} escape depth of promoter)

$\beta_2 = t/\lambda_{sp}$ (λ_{sp} is escape depth of support electron through the promoter)

With monolayer or less coverage of the promoter on the support the equation reduces to:

$$\left(\frac{I_p}{I_s}\right)_{exptl} = \left(\frac{p}{s}\right)_b \frac{D_{\epsilon p}\sigma_p\beta_1(1 + e^{-\beta_2})}{D_{es}\sigma_s 2(1 - e^{-\beta_2})} \tag{3}$$

Also, if the photoelectron lines have similar kinetic energies, the equation reduces to:

$$\left(\frac{I_p}{I_s}\right)_{exptl} = \left(\frac{p}{s}\right)_b \frac{\sigma_p\beta(1 - e^{-\beta})}{\sigma_s 2(1 - e^{-\beta})}$$

$$\beta = \beta_1 = \beta_2 \tag{4}$$

Kerkhof and Moulijn's model has been shown to agree with ESCA intensities reported in the literature. The model also allows one to predict the crystallite size of the supported material and to evaluate the escape depths and cross sections.

Some problems exist with the Kerkhof-Moulijn model. First an accurate escape depth for the component of the supported catalysts is difficult to obtain. However, it has been observed that the model is not sensitive to errors in the escape depths. For example, λ values of 1.3 and 1.8 nm were used for Al 2p photoelectrons from a Re/Al_2O_3 catalyst system. Both escape depth estimations fit the experimental data reasonably well within the experimental error. Secondly, nonuniform crystallite sizes will contribute to deviations from the model because one of the basic criteria of the supported catalyst models is uniform crystallite size. Lastly, inhomogeneous samples will deviate significantly from the model. Inhomogeneous coverage of the supports will cause variations in the relative intensities of the support and the promoter. These same factors that cause errors in this model can also affect models proposed for other systems analyzed by ESCA. Discussions on how to deal with these problems along with more complete reviews of quantitative ESCA are found in the literature.[20]

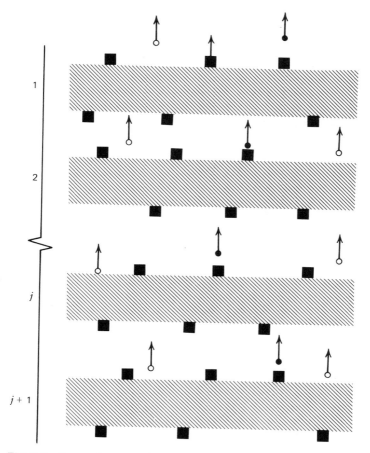

Figure 2. Proposed supported catalysts model of Kerkhof and Moulijn.[19]

2.3. Problems in Deconvolution and Curve Fitting

Since deconvolution and curve fitting are needed to perform quantitative analysis because of overlapping ESCA signals, it is felt that a few general comments about deconvolution and curve fitting are appropriate. The terms *deconvolution* and *curve fitting* have in the past been used interchangeably. However, they are not synonymous. Deconvolution is a process in which the broadening of a signal caused by instrumental effects is extracted from the true signal. With deconvolution, base-line resolution is not always obtained because the unbroadened signals may naturally overlap. Curve fitting, on the other hand, is a reconstruction of the natural lines from base line to fit the convolved envelop of signals. The problem in both cases is that no unique solution exists for an envelop. This has been pointed out by Wertheim[21] as regards deconvolution and by Hercules[22] as regards curve fitting. An example of the various parameters for curve fitting is shown in Figure 3. The main key to performing deconvolution or curve fitting is to have a thorough knowledge about the chemistry of the system and photoemission spectrum of the pure species of the convolved system. Therefore realistic parameters can be selected for the deconvolution and curve fitting so that the number of solutions are significantly reduced. In this manner a convincing and more reliable deconvolution or curve fit of the convolved spectrum

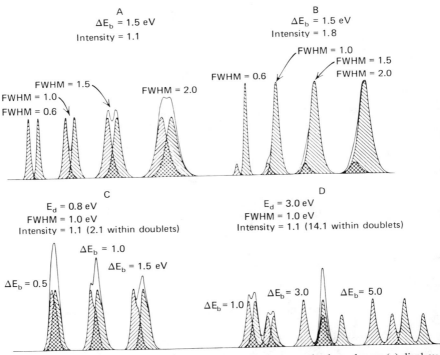

Figure 3. Examples of multiple solutions to curve fitting convolved envelopes: (*a*) displays the variation in peak convolution as the FWHM changes but the intensity and positions remain the same for a pair of singlet signals; (*b*) is the same as *a*, but the intensity ratio of the two peaks are 1:8 instead of 1:1 as in *a*; (*c*) displays the variation in peak convolution of two sets of doublets as their positions change, but the intensity, FWHM, and doublets splitting remains constant; (*d*) is the same as *c*, but the doublet splitting is larger and the doublet ratio is 14:1 instead of 2:1 as in *c* and the peaks are separated more than in *c*. (After Hercules.[22])

is obtained. Otherwise, these methods of peak separation and extraction become a random guessing game that prevents reasonable quantitation.

Curve fitting and deconvolution are best performed on a digital computer because of the lengthy and somewhat complex mathematics required by these methods. Also, digital computers process data with greater reliability and consistency than do analog devices. Curve fitting can also be performed on analog curve resolver instruments such as the Dupont 310 Curve Resolver. However, the results of this method rely heavily on the operator's ability. Therefore, a good deal of inconsistency can enter the results. Reviews of both curve fitting and deconsolution can be found in the literature.[22,24]

2.4. Referencing

A number of methods exist for referencing the binding energies of a photoemission spectrum. The first type of reference is an external standard. The most common external standard used is adventitious carbon; but, because the composition and electrical continuity between the carbon and the sample are not well known, this method of referencing can be somewhat unreliable. For example, the C 1s line is very reliable on pure metal foils; however, when used on alumina (an insulator) the C 1s line has been observed to shift 1 eV to higher binding energies.[25] Therefore, when this method is employed on catalysts, the measured binding energies that result may be lower than their true values. Therefore, some workers have tried using graphite mixed with their sample as a reference.[26] Graphite is used because it is electrically conductive and the chemical structure is well known. However, mixing does not ensure sample reproducibility and electrical continuity. Other materials have also been used as mixing standards such as metal oxides and inorganic salts.[27]

Another external referencing method is to vapor deposit a small amount of gold on a sample. The sample can then be referenced to the Au $4f$ photoemission lines. In this manner, the best electrical contact is most likely achieved. However, the possibility of differential charging between sample and reference still exists. Also, gold has been shown to react with some materials on which it was deposited.[28]

The second type of referencing is an internal standard method. An internal standard is a component of a sample that is chemically stable during experimentation and is chemically known. For example, the photoemission lines of supports in supported catalysts can sometimes be used as a reference, such as SiO_2 or Al_2O_3. In this case, the support and the promoter are in direct contact with each other. Also, the supports are chemically stable during such treatments as H_2 reductions. Many support binding energies have been reported in the literature. A list of binding energies (BE) for supports are found in Table 1 with references. However, one can check the binding energy of the support by vapor depositing

TABLE 1. Binding Energies for Supports

Support	ESCA line	BE (eV)	Reference
SiO_2	Si $2p$	103.1	41
$\gamma-Al_2O_3$	Al $2p$	74.5	42
TiO_2	Ti $2p_{3/2}$	458.5	43
ZrO_2	Zr $3d_{5/2}$	182.2	43
Cr_2O_3	Cr $2p_{3/2}$	576.6	44
ThO_2	Th $5d_{5/2}$	85.6	45

gold on the support and reference to the Au $4f$ lines. More detailed reviews of referencing are handled in the literature.[25] One must remember that when choosing a reference it must be in electrical contact with one's sample. Also, the reference must be chemically reliable and chemically stable throughout the entire experiment. Otherwise, the determination of chemical states can become difficult and meaningless.

2.5. Experimental Problems

Analysis Conditions

ESCA does present some experimental problems when used to analyze catalysts. First, the transfer of chemically reacted samples from a reactor into an ultrahigh-vacuum (UHV) system without exposure to air presents some difficulty. However, many UHV equipment manufacturers offer pretreatment chambers that can be attached directly to the ESCA spectrometer. For those instruments that are not readily adaptable to attached preparation chambers, a special sealable probe has been developed.[29] The sample can be treated on the sealable probe in a conventional catalytic reactor. After the reaction is complete, the probe is sealed and transported to the instrument, where it is pumped down to UHV in a differentially pumped insertion lock system prior to opening of the probe. A sample of a typical catalytic reactor with a sealable transport probe is shown in Figure 4.

High-surface-area catalysts tend to outgas for long periods when subjected to UHV. This problem is usually solved by using high-pumping-speed vacuum pumps such as turbo-molecular pumps.

Some workers have argued that analyzing catalysts under UHV and x-ray radiation is not representative of the catalysts under normal operating conditions. However, previous work has already shown that ESCA can provide complementary information to conventional gas adsorption methods for analyzing surfaces.[30] Thus, it can be argued that ESCA analyses are relevant. The experimentalist

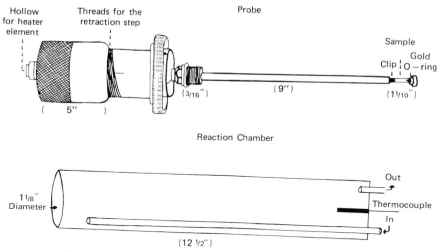

Figure 4.   Probe and reaction chamber. (After Patterson et al.[29])

should determine whether ESCA analyzing conditions have changed the samples because x-rays and UHV can, indeed, affect them. Effects such as x-ray reduction and x-ray degradation have been shown to occur in a few systems.[31,32] One method of determining changes under operating conditions is to analyze the time dependence of ESCA results. For example, to determine whether Cu(II) oxide is being photoreduced, the Cu $2p_{3/2}$ photoelectron line for Cu(II) oxide can be analyzed immediately after introduction of the sample in the instrument, then after ca. 10 min, scan the same photoelectron line over again. A variation in the Cu $2p_{3/2}$ ESCA spectrum should be taken as an indication of sample instability under x-ray radiation and vacuum.

Sample Charging

Sample charging is also a major problem in analyzing catalysts, especially supported catalysts. When electrons are photoejected from insulators, the positive charge induced by the ejection of photoelectrons cannot be compensated rapidly enough and therefore sample charging occurs. If similar charging occurred uniformly throughout the sample, no experimental difficulties would be encountered because the binding energies could be corrected for the amount of charging. However, the most prominent problem of charging is differential charging. Differential charging occurs when different areas or species of a sample charges different amounts. For example, if half of the Ni atoms on the surface Ni/Al$_2$O$_3$ catalysts charged 2.0 eV and the other half of the Ni atoms charged

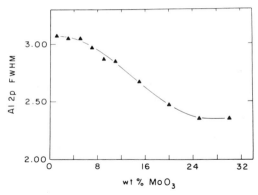

Figure 5. Correlation between Al 2*p* line width and percentage of MoO_3 for molybdena-alumina catalyst. (After Zingg et al.[34])

2.5 eV, the Ni photoelectron lines would be broader than if all the Ni atoms charged the same amount. Differential charging can occur from a few tenths of an electron volt, causing peak broadening, to a few electron volts, which results in multiple peaks.[33]

Zingg et al.[34] have shown that charging can depend on metal loading of supported catalysts. They analyzed various loadings of Mo/Al_2O_3. The Al 2*p* photoelectron line was used as an indicator of charging by measuring the full width at half-maximum (FWHM) of the line. A correlation between the Al 2*p* line width and the precentage of Mo loading was observed (Figure 5). As the loading of the Mo increased, the FWHM of the Al 2*p* line decreased. Therefore, a greater amount of charging occurred at lower loadings because the Al 2*p* line broadened at lower loadings. Also, the Mo $3d_{3/2,5/2}$ ESCA spectra of the same catalysts indicated that broadening increased as the loading decreased (Figure 6).

Since charging changes the apparent FWHM of Mo 3*d* signal, difficulty arises when one is attempting to assign a FWHM for curve fitting mixed signals. For example, in a reduction study of Mo/Al_2O_3, Patterson et al.[29] predicted that three Mo species existed after a 15-hr reduction in H_2 (Figure 7)—Mo(IV), Mo(V), Mo (VI)—based on a computer fit using a FWHM of the Mo 3*d* of 2.0 eV. The resultant weighted x^2 of this computer fit was 566. However, Zingg et al.[34] felt, based on charging effects, that a more realistic FWHM is 2.8 eV for the Mo 3*d*. Curve fitting using a FWHM of 2.8 for Mo 3*d* only produced two Mo species—Mo(V), Mo(IV). The resultant weighted x^2 was 92.5, a considerably better value. Therefore, the larger FWHM yielded a much better fit based on comparisons between the weighted x^2. Comparisons between Patterson and Zingg's curve fit are presented in Figure 7. Therefore, charging which can cause peak broadening of ESCA signal increases the difficulty in evaluating overlapping signals.

Mo 3d$_{3/2}$, $_{5/2}$

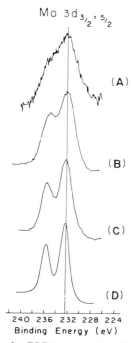

240 236 232 228 224
Binding Energy (eV)

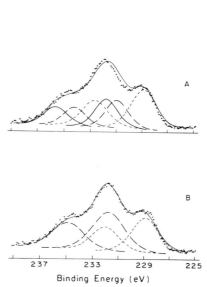

237   233   229   225
Binding Energy (eV)

Figure 6. ESCA spectra of molybdena-alumina catalyst, calcined at 500°C for 16 hr: (A) 1 wt% MoO_3/γ-Al_2O_3; (B) 11 wt% MoO_3/γ-Al_2O_3; (C) 30 wt% MoO_3/γ-Al_2O_3; (D) MoO_3. (After Zingg et al.[34])

Figure 7. Comparison of computer curve fit: (+) Experimental data; (−) computer fit (Solid line through data points); (−) Mo(VI); (- - -) Mo(V), - - - - (IV). (A) Using Patterson's parameters (2.0 − eV FWHM) (weighted x^2 = 566). (B) Using Zingg et al. parameters (2.8 − eV FWHM) (weighted x^2 = 92.5). (After Zingg et al.[34])

Particle Size

Variation in particle size of the supported species can affect the quantitation of the surface by ESCA.[5] Chin and Hercules (see Chin[6]) found that calcination temperature and/or the presence of Zn^{2+} were significant factors in varying the size of cobalt oxide crystallites formed on alumina. The crystallite sizes were estimated by x-ray diffraction line broadening. Catalysts of the same loading but different crystallite size were made by varying the calcination temperature or the amount of Zn^{2+} present. By plotting the Co/Al ESCA intensity ratios as a function of particle size, it was observed that the larger the particle size the smaller the Co/Al intensity ratio for the same catalyst loading. The variation in particle size can also be observed by ion-scattering spectroscopy (ISS) analysis (Figure 8).

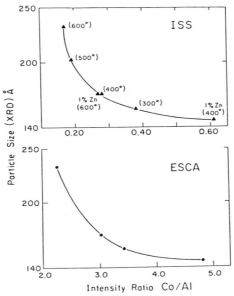

Figure 8. Influence of particle size on the observed ISS and ESCA intensity ratios. All catalysts contain 16% Co by weight. Samples doped with zinc are noted and values in parenthesis represent calcination temperature. (After Chin.[6])

These results are also in agreement with earlier experimental results of Brinen et al.[5] and theoretical work by Fung[4]. The change of ESCA intensity ratios is caused by the limited escape depth of the photoejected electrons. The intensity ratio of Co/Al decreases as the Co particle size increases because the electrons ejected from the central part of the Co particle do not have the ability to escape and be detected. This result is in support of the criteria for consistent crystallite size in Kerkhof and Moulijn's quantitative supported catalysts model,[19] discussed earlier. Therefore, variations in particle size must be considered when quantitative comparisons are made between catalysts of different loadings and calcination temperature.

2.6. Binding Energies

Binding energies are an important parameter that an experimentalist needs to measure by ESCA because of the highly useful information that they provide. In a large number of cases the binding energies for an element show chemical shifts which are characteristic of that element's chemical state.

In some cases the chemical shift occurs in a systematic fashion as the oxidation state changes. For example, aluminum shows chemical shifts which proceed from low to high binding energy as the chemical state changes from Al^0 to Al^{3+}. The reason why binding energy shifts in this manner is because the ejected electrons from the Al^{3+} are subject to less electron shielding from the valence electrons and a greater net positive charge from the atom than the ejected electrons from Al^0. Unfortunately, binding-energy chemical shifts depend on other factors such as electron relaxation and extra- and intraatomic forces. These effects make it difficult to predict chemical shifts from zero-order considerations. For example, Co metal has the lowest binding energy of all Co chemical states. The binding energies of the Co $2p$ electrons increase from Co to Co^{+2} which is predictable. However, Co_3O_4 has a lower binding energy than CoO and a higher binding energy than the metal.[35] Therefore, to evaluate the chemical nature of species on catalyst surfaces, reference compounds must be examined by ESCA to determine the chemical shifts of the different compounds. Then by comparing the binding energies of the catalyst to a series of standard compounds, one is able to obtain a reasonable characterization of the chemical states of an element on a surface. However, even this method of characterization does not always work because many of the possible compounds on a catalyst can have either the same or very similar binding energies. Therefore, frequently one must rely on other characteristics of the photoelectron spectrum to determine the chemical character of the catalyst. For example, the binding energy shift for $Cu^0 \rightarrow Cu^{1+}$ of the $2p_{3/2}$ line is only –0.4 eV and therefore not easily distinguishable.[36] Hence, to distinguish between these chemical states another method must be employed besides using reference compounds.

The best way of handling the chemical state determination of the example just illustrated is to use the Auger parameter method.[37] This method distinguishes chemical states by observing the energy separation between photoelectron lines and Auger lines of an element. We have chosen Zn to illustrate Auger parameters; however, the same method can be applied to Cu. Zinc metal $2p_{2/3}$ and the *LMM* Auger lines are separated by 523.1 eV and the separation for ZnO is 528.9 eV using aluminum $K\alpha$ x-rays. Therefore, the difference between the Auger parameters of Zn and ZnO is 3.2 eV. This is appreciably better than the 0.2-eV shifts between the Zn $2p_{3/2}$ lines of ZnO and Zn.[38] Also, this method eliminates the need for an outside binding energy reference because the chemical states are determined by peak separation, not absolute binding energies. The reason why a reference such as the C $1s$ line is not needed when Auger parameters are used is because the chemical states are not determined by referencing to a standard binding energy. Instead, a two-dimensional array is constructed by plotting the binding energy of the most intense photoelectron line on the x axis and the kinetic energy of the most intense Auger line on the y axis for a series of known compounds (Figure 9). Therefore, characterization is performed by location of a

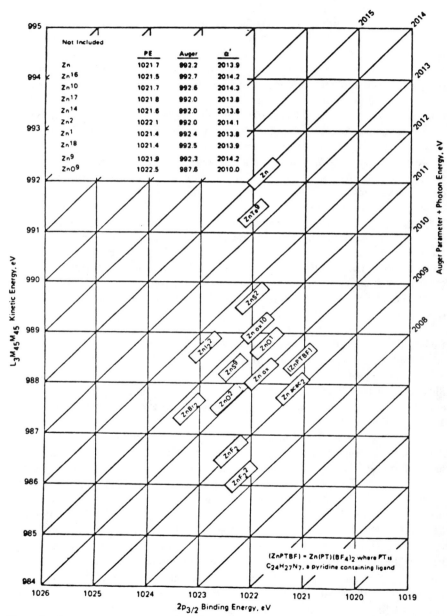

Figure 9.   Example of the Zn two-dimensional Auger parameter array. (After Wagner et al.[37])

point on the two-dimensional array instead of determining the absolute binding energies of the photoelectron lines and Auger lines. The Auger parameter method, however, is not applicable to all elements.

The satellite structure of photoelectron lines often contains a good deal of chemical information. Satellites become vary useful when binding energies and Auger parameters fail to distinguish chemical states. The most important satellite peaks examined for chemical information are the shakeup satellites that lie at binding energies higher than the main signal. Just the presence or absence of a satellite signal can indicate a certain chemical state. Copper metal and Cu_2O does not have a shakeup satellite signal for the $2p_{3/2}$ line; however, CuO does have a distinct shakeup satellite structure[26] (Figure 10). Therefore, just by initial inspection of the Cu $2p_{3/2}$, the existence of CuO can be determined. However, caution must be used in this kind of evaluation because a different compound

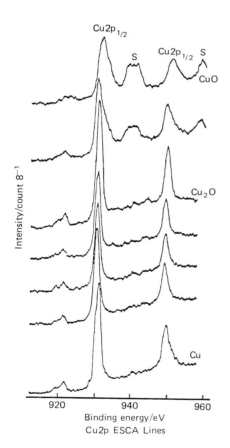

Figure 10. Cu $2p_{3/2,1/2}$ ESCA spectra of Cu, Cu_2O, and CuO. Here, **S** represents satellite.

with the same chemical state may not have a similar shakeup satellite. For example, CuO has a satellite, but CuS does not.[39]

Along similar lines, it has been observed that the satellite structure can be compound dependent. Therefore, chemical characterization in some cases can be evaluated on the basis of satellite shape. For example, the Co in Co/Al_2O_3 is a classic example of analyzing variation in satellite structure and intensity.[40] The difficulty in analyzing the oxidic cobalt alumina catalyst is to differentiate between Co_3O_4 and CoO on the surface of the catalyst. This problem results because the binding-energy shifts of the Co 2p line are not large enough to provide absolute confirmation of the species with most conventional ESCA systems. However, the satellite structures of these two species are sufficiently different to be useful as diagnostic tools. The Co_3O_4 and the CoO $2p_{1/2}$ ESCA spectra are shown in Figure 11. We can see quite clearly that the shakeup satellite are significantly different for Co_3O_4 and CoO. The intensity of the satellite for Co_3O_4 is about 20% of the main line; for CoO it is about 80% of the main signal. Also, the separations between the main peak and the satellite are different. Therefore, the satellite position and more importantly the ratios between the satellite and main signals give a clear criterion in distinguishing between CoO and Co_3O_4.

A good deal of preliminary work, both theoretical and experimental, must be done before actual experimentation on catalysts by ESCA can be performed. However, after such preliminary groundwork is completed, a substantial amount of information can be obtained by ESCA. We hope to indicate this in the application section that follows.

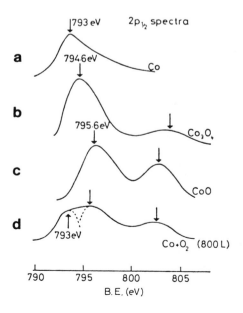

Figure 11.   Co $2p_{3/2}$ ESCA spectra of (a) Co; (b) Co_3O_4; (c) CoO; and (d) Co exposed to 800 L of O_2. (After Moyers and Roberts.[35])

3. SPECIFIC APPLICATIONS

We will now discuss the applications of ESCA to catalysis, looking at some specific uses of ESCA to understand catalytic systems. Most of the research that appears in the literature focuses on the dependence of the chemical states and concentrations of surface species as a function of catalyst preparation and treatment. For example, workers have examined how calcination temperature affects surface states and concentration by examining the surface of supported catalysts of the same loading at different calcination temperatures.[46] Also, reduction studies using flowing H_2 have been run at different times and temperatures to investigate the reducibility of the promoter on a support.[47] The information derived from ESCA is then compared with data derived from other techniques to arrive at a picture of the surface chemistry and structure of heterogeneous catalysts.

3.1. Supported Ni Catalysts

Because the need to produce synthesis gas has become important in the past few years, studies of Ni catalysts have increased substantially. Synthesis gas (CO/H_2) exposed to metallic nickel will convert primarily to methane with small amounts of higher molecular weight hydrocarbons. The major portion of work performed by surface analysis on nickel catalysts has been geared toward supported nickel catalysts.[46-51]

The main objective of the supported nickel research using ESCA is to understand the metal–support interaction. Many workers are concerned with how catalyst preparation affects the metal–support interaction. To investigate this interaction, hydrogen reduction at elevated temperatures was employed. The extent of the interaction is assumed to be inversely proportional to the reducibility of the supported metal. In other words, the greater the reducibility of the supported metal, the weaker the interaction between the metal and support. Vedrine et al.[47] analyzed a series of supported nickel catalysts of different supports to evaluate their relative metal–support interaction. By determining the extent of reduction of surface Ni using ESCA, the following series of reducibility was determined:

$$\text{no support} > TiO_2 > SiO_2 \sim SiO_2\text{-}Al_2O_3 \sim Al_2O_3 > MgO$$

However, Vedrine et al. did not provide a clear indication of whether the Ni/SiO_2 reduced more easily than the Ni/Al_2O_3. Hercules and colleagues have extensively analyzed a number of different Ni loadings on Al_2O_3 and SiO_2 (see Wu and Hercules[46] and Shyu and Hercules[48]). Through the synergistic use of ESCA and ISS, the SiO_2 support afforded a more reducible Ni catalyst than did Al_2O_3. Before reduction, the Ni on SiO_2 was determined to be present only as NiO. How-

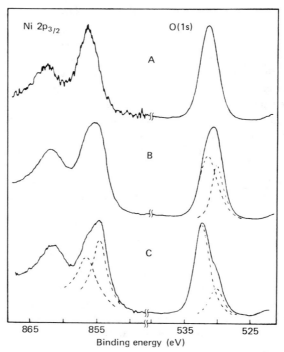

Figure 12. Ni $2p_{3/2}$ and O $1s$ spectra of supported nickel catalysts. (*a*) 7% Ni on γ-alumina, calcined at 600°C. The binding energies were as follows: Ni $2p_{3/2}$, 856.2 eV (FWHM 3.6 eV); O $1s$, 531.1 eV (FWHM 3.1 eV). (*b*) 23.9% Ni on γ-alumina, calcined at 600°C. The binding energies were as follows: Ni $2p_{3/2}$, 855.2 eV (FWHM 4.6 eV); O $1s$, 530.7 eV (FWHM 3.4 ev). (*c*) 26% Ni on silica, calcined at 400°C. The binding energies were as follows: Ni $2p_{3/2}$, 854.4 and 856.5 eV (curve resolved); O $1s$, 532.2 and 530.0 eV (deconvoluted). (After Wu and Hercules.[46])

ever, the Al_2O_3 support displayed two strong interaction species at less than monolayer coverage. The interaction species were evaluated to be Ni^{2+} ion in the tetrahedral and octahedral sites of the Al_2O_3. Therefore, the Al_2O_3 displays much stronger metal–support interaction than does the SiO_2 support. Figures 12 and 13 and Tables 2 and 3 display the differences between the metal–support interaction of Al_2O_3 and SiO_2. For the SiO_2 support the nickel on the surface has the same binding energy and peak shape as NiO does at all loadings, even above monolayer coverage. Also, at high nickel loading, an additional oxygen signal at lower binding energy is observed. This signal is attributed to NiO species. On Al_2O_3 catalyst, however, the nickel changes character at different loadings. Figure 12 and Table 2 indicate that the binding energy of the Ni $2p_{3/2}$ is decreasing from 856.1 to 854.8 as the loading changes from below monolayer coverage (2%) to above monolayer coverage (33%). Also, the Ni $2p_{3/2}$ signal at low load-

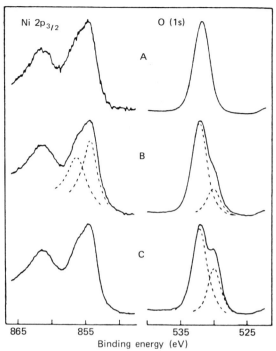

Figure 13. Ni $2p_{3/2}$ and O $1s$ spectra of nickel catalysts supported on silica. (*a*) 4% Ni on silica, calcined at 400°C. The binding energies were as follows: Ni $2p_{3/2}$, 856.3 and 854.5 eV (deconvoluted); O $1s$, 532.1 eV. (*b*) 26% Ni on silica, calcined at 400°C. The binding energies were as follows: Ni $2p_{3/2}$ 856.5 and 854.7 eV (curve resolved); O $1s$, 532.2 and 530.3 (curved resolved). (*c*) 35% Ni on silica, calcined at 400°C. The binding energies were as follows: Ni $2p_{3/2}$, 856.4 and 854.5 eV (deconvoluted); O $1s$, 532.1 and 530.1 eV (curve resolved). (After Wu and Hercules.[46])

ings does not resemble the NiO spectra; however, the higher loading does. Therefore, the Ni species on the surface Al_2O_3 is changing as the loading is increased, but the Ni on SiO_2 support does not change.

In addition to pure supports, Houalla and Delmon have investigated Ni supported on SiO_2-Al_2O_3 mixed gels.[49] By varying the amount of Al_2O_3 in the gel, it was observed that Al_2O_3 increases the dispersion of Ni on the surface of the catalysts. This was concluded because the ESCA nickel/support intensity ratio increased as the amount of Al_2O_3 was increased in the support for the same loading of Ni. In addition, using Al_2O_3 as a support gave rise to higher activities and greater stability under methanation conditions than did pure silica. These properties were attributed to higher dispersion of the Ni and stronger metal-support interaction with alumina.

An alternative method of making supported Ni catalysts is by coprecipitation

TABLE 2.   Binding Energies and Full Width at Half-Maxima (FWHM) of
Nickel–Alumina Catalysts for Different Nickel Contents

Ni content[a] (%)	ESCA binding energies[b] (eV)		
	Ni $2p_{3/2}$	O $1s$	C $1s$
2	856.1 (3.2 eV)	531.1 (3.1 eV)	284.7
7	856.2 (3.6 eV)	531.1 (3.1 eV)	284.9
10	856.1 (3.9 eV)	531.1 (3.1 eV)	284.9
13.6	855.7 (4.0 eV)	531.1 (3.1 eV)	284.8
20	855.6 (4.4 eV)	530.9 (3.2 eV)	285.1
23.9	855.2 (4.6 eV)	530.7 (3.4 eV)	285.0
33.2	854.8 (4.4 eV)	530.3 (3.2 eV)	—

[a]Catalysts were supported on γ-alumina, calcined at 600°C for 5 hr.
[b]FWHM values are given in parentheses. All binding energies are relative to Al $2p$ peak taken at 74.5 eV.

of the support and the metal. Shalvoy et al.[50,51] have used ESCA to determine the degree of metal–support interaction in coprecipitated Ni catalyst. Through a hydrogen reduction study, Shalvoy et al. determined that coprecipitated Ni catalysts possess a greater degree of interaction than the corresponding impregnated catalysts. Even for loadings up to 40 wt% Ni, $NiAl_2O_4$ was observed. Also, $NiSiO_3$ was found on the surface of coprecipitated silica catalysts but was not found on the impregnated SiO_2 support. Therefore, through the use of ESCA, metal–support interactions for the nickel system were shown to depend on both the support and the method of preparation.

Studies of nickel catalysts after methanation exposure have been limited. However, some nickel single-crystal work has been performed. Goodman et al.[52] analyzed reacted supported catalysts by Auger electron spectroscopy (AES) and compared the results with reacted Ni ⟨100⟩ single crystal. By measuring the methanation turnover numbers and analyzing the surfaces of the supported nickel and single crystal, it was concluded that the reaction kinetics of the single crystal resembled that of the supported catalysts. Therefore, through electron

TABLE 3. Binding Energies and Full Width at Half-Maxima (FWHM) of Nickel–Silica Catalysts for Different Nickel Contents

Ni content[a] (%)	ESCA binding energies[b] (eV)		
	Ni $2p_{3/2}$	O $1s$	Si $2s$
4	854.7 (4.7 eV)	532.1 (2.8 eV)	153.9
8	854.8 (4.6 eV)	532.1 (2.8 eV)	153.9
10	854.9 (4.7 eV)	532.1 (2.8 eV)	153.9
15	854.9 (4.6 eV)	532.1 (2.8 eV)	153.9
20	854.7 (4.5 eV)	532.1 (2.8 eV)	153.9
26	854.7 (4.7 eV)	532.2 (4)[c] 530.0 (1)[c]	154.0
35	854.7 (4.6 eV)	532.1 (2)[c] 530.1 (1)[c]	153.8

[a]Catalysts were supported on silica, calcined at 400°C for 5 hr.
[b]FWWM values are given in parentheses. All binding energy values are relative to Si $2p$ peak taken at 102.9 eV.
[c]Relative intensities are in parentheses.

spectroscopy the analysis of well-characterized single crystals may reveal the characteristics of the real supported catalysts.

3.2. Supported Co Catalysts

The surface characterization of Co/Al_2O_3 catalysts has also been studied by ESCA. As for the nickel system, the chemical nature of the surface and the metal–support interaction are of prime interest. Co/Al_2O_3 catalysts are used for hydrocracking. However, cobalt is also used as a promoter in hydrodesulfurization cataylsts (i.e., Mo/Al_2O_3). Therefore, a clear understanding of Co/Al_2O_3 will aid in evaluating the $Co-Mo/Al_2O_3$ catalytic system.

Grimblot, Bonnelle, and coworkers[40,53-55] performed a good deal of the initial ESCA work on Co catalysts. First they examined the cobalt–oxygen system.[40,53] By analyzing the satellite intensity and structure of the Co $2p_{1/2,3/2}$ signals, they were able to both distinguish and quantify the Co-O system. Moyers and

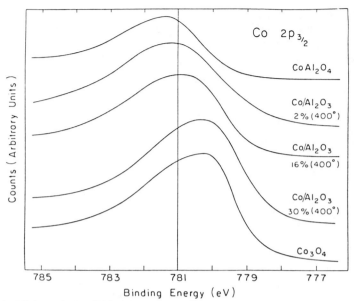

Figure 14. High-resolution ESCA spectra of Co/Al_2O_3 catalysts after calcination at 400°C in air for 5 hr. Spectra were taken using a HP 5950A electron spectrometer. (After Chin.[6])

Roberts[35] were able to employ the method of Bonnelle et al.[54] as a diagnostic tool in analyzing the cobalt interaction with oxygen, water, and carbon monoxide. Grimblot et al.[40,55] extended these studies by analyzing the $Co-Mo/Al_2O_3$ catalyst system. Based on satellite analysis they determined that below monolayer coverage the Co^{2+} ions only occupies the tetrahedral sites of the alumina. After monolayer coverage Co_3O_4 appears on the surface. Also, when the Co content is less than 0.5% and the atomic ratio of Mo/Co is less than 4, the supported cobalt is not influenced by the Mo. Grimblot et al.[55] proposed, however, that when the Co content increases to 1% a new phase form of the Mo–Co system occurs, namely, Mo_4Co.

Chin and Hercules[56] have also observed that the loading of Co affects the surface species of the Co/Al_2O_3 catalysts. This was concluded by observing the chemical shift of the Co $2p_{3/2}$ ESCA signal as a function of Co loading (Figure 14). At low loadings (i.e., 1–5 wt% Co) the position of the Co $2p_{3/2}$ corresponded to $CoAl_2O_4$. At higher loadings (i.e., 5–12 wt% Co) the Co $2p_{3/2}$ signal shifted to lower binding energies. When the loading was increased above monolayer coverage the binding energy shifted to its lowest position, which corresponded to Co_3O_4. Also, when the Co $2p_{3/2}$/Al $2p$ intensity ratio was plotted as a function of loading, a linear relationship was obtained with a discontinuity

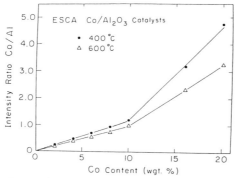

Figure 15. ESCA peak area intensity ratios (Co/Al) versus metal content for catalysts calcined at 400°C and 600°C. (After Chin.[6])

in slope at greater than monolayer coverage (Figure 15). It was concluded that, as the cobalt content increased, the tetrahedral sites in Al_2O_3 are filled first, then the octahedral sites were filled. After monolayer coverage the surface became covered with Co_3O_4. An EXAFS study supports these findings.[57] As the loading of the catalysts increased, the average Co coordination number increased (see Table 4), which supports the idea that the tetrahedral sites of the Al_2O_3 are filled first and then the octahedral sites.

From this same study, the calcination temperature was determined to affect the surface concentration and the degree of metal–support interaction. By examining the Co $2p_{3/2}$/Al $2p$ ESCA signal ratios for the same loadings but different calcination temperatures, it was determined that, as the calcination temperature increased, the Co $2p_{3/2}$/Al $2p$ ratio decreased (Figure 15). Also, at higher calcination temperatures, Co was found to be less reducible than the catalysts calcined at lower temperature (Figure 15). Therefore, because the Co $2p_{3/2}$/Al $2p$ ratio de-

TABLE 4. Summary of EXAFS Results

Sample	Average coordination number $(\bar{N})^a$	Bond lengths (Å)^b
20% Co (600°C)	4.9	1.84
12% Co (600°C)	5.1	1.78
12% Co (400°C)	5.5	1.84
6% Co (400°C)	4.1	1.84
2% Co (600°C)	3.5	1.78

$^a\bar{N}$ was measured with an uncertainty of ±20%.
^{b}Bond lengths were measured with a precision of ±0.05 Å.

creased and less reducibility was observed for higher calcination temperatures, it was concluded that the higher calcination temperatures favor migration of the Co ions into the bulk of the Al_2O_3, which increases the interaction species on the surface of the catalysts. Hence, lower loadings and higher calcination temperatures favor greater metal–support interaction, therefore favoring $CoAl_2O_4$ formation, whereas higher loadings and lower calcination temperatures favor less metal–support interaction on the surface of the Co/Al_2O_3 catalyst system.

3.3 Supported Mo Catalysts

Of all the catalysts analyzed by ESCA, the Mo/Al_2O_3 and $Co-Mo/Al_2O_3$ systems have been most extensively studied. Mo and Co–Mo catalysts are primarily used for hydrodesulfurization reactions for the removal of sulfur from oil feedstocks. Both the oxidic and sulfided forms of the catalysts have been studied.

The method of preparing Mo catalysts involves impregnation of ammonium paramolybdate on a support, which is then dried and calcined. At this point of the preparation, the catalyst is considered in the oxidic state. Using ESCA, it was found that the binding energies of the Mo peaks on the oxidic catalysts are either the same[29,58] as or slightly higher than[59,60] that of MoO_3. The higher binding energies have been interpreted as a strong metal–support interaction caused by partial electron transfer from the Mo—O bond to the aluminum[59] or a displacement of the alumina in the alumina lattice by the molybdenum atoms.[61] Also, the Mo peaks were broadened compared to pure MoO_3 ESCA spectra.[59,62] The broadening has been attributed to electron transfer.[59] However, others believed that the broadening is due to three distinct Mo species present on the surface that could not be resolved.[62] As discussed earlier, Zingg et al.[34] determined that the broadening was attributed to sample charging which resulted in broadening of the peaks and shifting the peak maxima to higher binding energies.

ESCA cannot distinguish between MoO_3 and $Al_2(MoO_4)_3$ because the binding energies are the same. Therefore, to examine if an interaction species existed laser Raman spectroscopy (LRS) was employed. Zingg et al.[34] determined that three distinct molybdenum species existed: an interactive species, $Al_2(MoO_4)_3$ and bulk MoO_3. The amount of each species depends on loading and calcination temperature.

Reduction studies of Mo/Al_2O_3 catalysts that investigated the metal–support interaction have triggered some interesting controversy. Pure MoO_3 has been shown to reduce completely to Mo^{4+} under high-temperature (i.e., 500°C) flowing H_2.[63] Early work[29,64] indicated that Mo/Al_2O_3 would reduce to a mixture of Mo^{6+}, Mo^{5+}, and Mo^{4+}. However, it has been argued that only two species exist after reduction (i.e., Mo^{5+}, Mo^{4+}) when charging effects from an insulator are considered.[34] In a time-dependent reduction study, it was determined by ESCA, which was corrected for charging, that the MO^{6+} was reduced

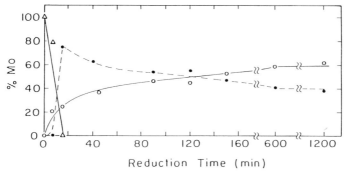

Figure 16. Mo oxidation state as a function of reduction time for the 15 wt% MoO_3 catalysts. Reduction was carried out at 500°C in H_2. Key: triangles, Mo^{6+}; solid circles, Mo^{5+}; open circles, Mo^{4+}. (After Zingg et al.[34])

to both Mo^{5+} and Mo^{4+} within 20 min at 500°C in hydrogen (Figure 16) for a 15 wt% MoO_3 catalyst. Therefore, based on the reductive behavior of pure MoO_3, the Mo^{4+} present on the reduced catalyst is a result of the reduction of octahedrally coordinated Mo^{6+}. This was substantiated by leaching away the MoO_3 on Mo/Al_2O_3 with NH_4OH, which will only remove the Mo^{6+} octahedral species, and then reduce the leached oxidic catalysts. The reduced leached catalysts only consisted of Mo^{5+} on the surface (Figure 17). Therefore, since leaching results in the removal of only MoO_3 (octahedral Mo^{6+}) and the peak due to Mo^{4+} is almost completely absent after leaching and reduction, it was concluded that the production of Mo^{4+} is a result of reduction of octahedral MO^{6+} and that the Mo^{5+} is a result of reducing the tetrahedrally coordinated Mo^{6+}. These results are also consistent with those of Masson et al.[65] and DuFaux et al.,[66] who have indicated that low-loading molybdenum catalysts favor tetrahedral filling and that at higher loadings the octahedral sites of the Al_2O_3 are filled. A proposed model based on ESCA and supporting analysis is presented in Figure 18. Figure 18 indicates a monomeric[67-69] and a dimeric[70] molybdenum species for less than monolayer coverage. At above monolayer coverage, formation of MoO_3 and $Al_2(MoO_4)_3$ has been confirmed by LRS.[34]

In an attempt to determine the hydrodesulfurization mechanism, workers have used ESCA to characterize the surface of the Mo/Al_2O_3 after sulfiding.[71,72] H_2S and CS_2 were used to sulfide the catalysts. The most common hydrodesulfurization reactions are described by the following:

$$\text{(thiophene)}_S + H_2 \rightarrow H_2S + CH_3CH_2CH_2CH_3$$

$$CS_2 + H_2 \longrightarrow H_2S + CH_4$$

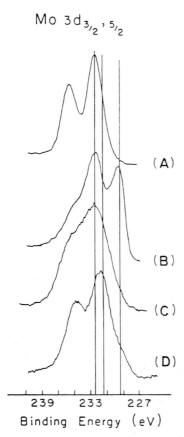

Mo $3d_{3/2,5/2}$

(A)

(B)

(C)

(D)

239   233   227

Binding Energy (eV)

Figure 17. Mo $3d_{3/2,5/2}$ ESCA spectra of 30 wt% MoO_3/Al_2O_3 catalysts: (A) oxidic catalysts; (B) reduced catalysts (H_2, 500°C for 12 hr); (C) leached oxidic catalysts (3% NH_4OH solution until constant Mo/Al ratio; (D) catalysts leached (3% NH_4OH solution), then reduced (same as B and C). (After Zingg et al.[34])

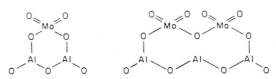

Figure 18. Proposed structure of the surface of Mo/Al_2O_3.

174

Okamoto et al.[72] have recently attributed the thiophene conversion per gram of MoO_3 to the degree of sulfiding. This was concluded by determining the S/Mo(IV) atomic ratio on the surface by ESCA. When the S/Mo(IV) ratio was equal to unity, maximum activity for conversion of thiophene was observed. They proposed the following active species:

□ is an anion vacancy

On the basis of their findings, Okamoto et al. proposed a possible reaction mechanism for the Mo/Al_2O_3 as a redox cycle between Mo(IV) and Mo(VI). The proposal appears consistent with Zingg and co-worker's reduction studies[34] of the oxidic catalysts and their conclusion that the Mo(VI) is converted to Mo(IV) under reducing condition. The proposed mechanism reaction is depicted in Figures 19 and 20.

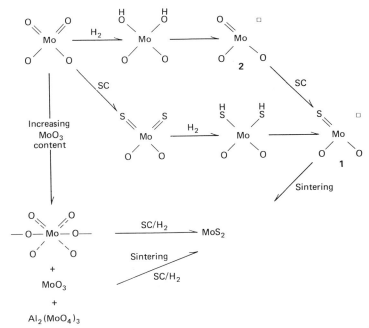

Figure 19. Proposed processes in producing the anion vacancy. SC represents a sulfur compound such as CS_2 or thiophene. (After Okamoto et al.[82])

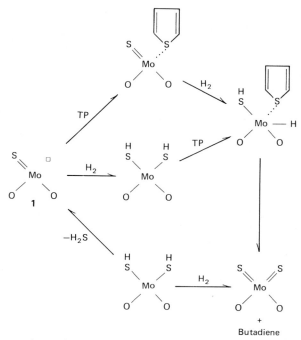

Figure 20. Proposed reaction mechanism for hydrodesulfurization of thiophene (TP). (After Okamoto et al.[82])

3.4. Supported Co–Mo

The Co–Mo/Al$_2$O$_3$ hydrodesulfurization catalyst has received more attention in recent years than the Mo/Al$_2$O$_3$ catalysts. The Co–Mo/Al$_2$O$_3$ system is more important from an industrial standpoint because it exhibits greater stability and activity for hydrodesulfurization than the unpromoted system. Of all the catalyst systems studied by ESCA, Co–Mo/Al$_2$O$_3$ catalysts appear in the literature more than any other.

The structure of the Co–Mo/Al$_2$O$_3$ system has been shown to depend on the preparation method used:[73] (1) cobalt impregnated first, then the molybdenum; (2) molybdenum impregnated first, then the cobalt; and (3) the Co and Mo impregnated simultaneously. ESCA analysis indicates different surface characteristics appear for each method of preparation. However, the chemical states of the oxidic catalysts of all the preparation are the same (MoO$_3$, Co$_3$O$_4$ and CoAl$_2$O$_4$).[73] Also, the amount of Co$_3$O$_4$ was found to increase with Co loading.[73] This result is consistent with work performed on Co/Al$_2$O$_3$ catalysts by Chin and Hercules.[56] However, some workers have indicated that methods

2 and 3 contain an interaction species between the Co and Mo believed to be $CoMoO_4$.[73,74] Workers have observed bulk $CoMoO_4$ on catalysts prepared using method 2 by LRS and by x-ray diffraction.[74] In contradiction to these findings, Cimino and DeAngelis[75] have excluded the possibility of $CoMoO_4$ interaction species because the reducibility of the $Co-Mo/Al_2O_3$ catalysts was less than bulk $CoMoO_4$. Both α-$CoMoO_4$ and β-$CoMoO_4$ compounds were reduced at 400°C in hydrogen, then analyzed by ESCA. Both $CoMoO_4$ species reduced to metal Mo and some Co metal. However, the Mo did not reduce past Mo^{4+}, and only a small amount of Co reduction was observed on the catalyst.[75]

Workers using ESCA have shown that the amount of Co_3O_4 on the Co-Mo/Al_2O_3 catalysts for the same loading depended on the method of preparation.[76] When the Co and Mo were coimpregnated, the catalysts contained the greatest amount of Co_3O_4. When the Mo was impregnated first, the catalysts had a lesser amount of Co_3O_4 than the coimpregnated catalysts. When the Co was impregnated first, the oxidic catalysts had the least Co_3O_4 on the surface.

Okamoto et. al. also used ESCA to determine that the sequentially impregnated catalysts form layers.[76] The layering is brought about by the second impregnation covering the first. The simultaneous impregnation has been observed to form separate phases on the surface.[76] Grimblot et al.[40] used ESCA to determine that the Co^{2+} ions preferentially occupy the tetrahedral sites of the Al_2O_3 for the $Co-Mo/Al_2O_3$ catalysts. This conclusion is consistent with studies of the Co/Al_2O_3 catalysts[56] and also with the dependence of Co_3O_4 formation on preparation method.

Okamoto et al.[77] have proposed a catalytic process for hydrodesulfurization by $Co-Mo/Al_2O_3$ similar to the model of Mo/Al_2O_3 based on ESCA results.[77] However, this work has been criticized by other workers because Okamoto et al. performed their experiments under static conditions.[78] Okamoto and associates' study indicated that under sulfiding static conditions the Co was reduced to the metal. However, Patterson et al.[29] have indicated the presence of a cobalt sulfide species under flowing conditions instead of Co metal. Brinen et al. also agrees that Co metal is not present under these conditions.[79] Moreover, Co metal has been shown to be unstable at high-temperature sulfiding conditions (H_2/H_2S).[80] DeBeer et al.[81], using a flowing system, observed that the S/Mo ratio is much greater than that obtained by Okamoto and co-workers, which would indicate that the Co was being sulfided. In a later publication, Okamoto et al.,[82] using a dynamic sulfiding system, have confirmed the presence of a cobalt sulfide species by ESCA on the $Co-Mo/Al_2O_3$ catalyst.

3.5. Concluding Remarks on Supported Catalysts

Besides the four supported catalytic systems already discussed, many other supported catalysts have also been studied in some detail by ESCA in conjunction with other techniques. For example, Ni–W/Al$_2$O$_3$,[83] Cu/Al$_2$O$_3$,[84] Re/Al$_2$O$_3$,[85] and Pd/Al$_2$O$_3$,[86] with various promoters, have been analyzed by ESCA. Primarily, workers are using ESCA on the other supported systems in the same manner as we have shown in the previous examples. The characterization of chemical states and concentration of the surface species are of prime interest, as are investigations of preparation treatments and metal–support interactions in many of the supported systems. ESCA has supplied a great deal of information about the supported catalyst systems. However, because ESCA has a number of limitations, some conclusions based only on ESCA results can be misleading without substantiating data obtained by other techniques.

3.6. Unsupported Heterogeneous Catalysis

Unsupported catalysts have not received as much attention as supported catalysts from surface spectroscopists. Also, the unsupported systems are more varied than the supported systems. Therefore, because of the variety of these catalysts and the limited amount of work performed on them, we have decided to present only two selected examples of how ESCA has been used to study unsupported catalyst systems.

Both systems to be discussed below are methanation catalysts: (1) nickel intermetallic catalayst (ThNi$_5$, UNi$_5$, ZrNi$_5$) and (2) Raney nickel catalysts. In both cases, ESCA analysis can be performed with ease because both are electrically conductive samples. Therefore, problems such as charging (noted in the supported catalysts) are not present.

Nickel Intermetallic Compounds

Nickel intermetallic compounds such as ThNi$_5$, UNi$_5$, and ZrNi$_5$ have become scientifically important because of their use as permanent magnets, hydrogen-storage devices, and heterogeneous catalysts. LaNi$_5$ was one of the first rare earth intermetallics to be studied as a catalyst because of its efficient ability to store hydrogen.[87-90] Later, it was discovered that other nickel intermetallic systems (ThNi$_5$ and UNi$_5$) were also active methanation catalysts. However, they do not have the ability to store large quantities of hydrogen.[89,91] Therefore, interest in intermetallic surface characteristics arose because of the catalytic hydrogenation ability of the nonhydrogen storage Ni intermetallics.

ESCA studies of LaNi$_5$ have determined that the surface of this intermetallic consists of La$_2$O$_3$, La(OH)$_2$, and small amounts of metallic Ni.[92] The bulk remained as LaNi$_5$. Initial studies by Chin et al.[93] also determined that some metallic surface nickel remained when the rare-earth intermetallics were oxidized. An interesting aspect of this study is that the surface of ThNi$_5$ resembles that of nickel supported on ThO$_2$ before catalytic reactions. However, ThNi$_5$ displays a much higher methanation activity than does Ni supported on ThO$_2$ (see Table 5).

TABLE 5. Catalytic Behavior of the Catalysts Studied

Catalyst[a]	Percentage of CO converted at 300°C	Surface Area (m²/g)	
		Before reaction	After reaction
ThNi$_5$	~100	0.25	18
UNi$_5$	12.5	~0.2	30
ZrNi$_5$	5.3	~0.2	28
Ni/ThO$_2$	Negligible	2.8	2.4
ThCo$_5$[b]	<50	0.03	42.7
ThCo$_5$[b,c]	93.3	—	—

[a] Samples were reduced for 2 hr prior to the methanation reaction.
[b] Reaction gas mixture was ca. 1:1 CO:H$_2$
[c] Reduction and reaction temperature was 450°C.

By using ESCA to examine the surface of the intermetallic after synthesis gas treatment, a correlation between catalytic activity and surface composition of the catalysts was postulated. When each of the intermetallics was treated with H$_2$ at 300°C and then reacted with synthesis gas, the nickel concentration increased relative to the rare-earth component on the surface. However, under similar conditions the Ni on Ni/ThO$_2$ catalysts decreased relative to the ThO$_2$ (Table 6). These determinations are performed by comparing ratios of the Ni $2p_{3/2}$ signal to the most intense ESCA line of the "support" element before and after treatment. The results of this simple experiment directly correlate with the catalytic activity. The intermetallic with the greatest enrichment of nickel on the surface (ThNi$_5$) after treatment displayed the greatest catalytic activity. Also, the sample with the smallest increase in surface Ni (Ni/ThO$_2$) exhibited the lowest activity. The relative increase of nickel on the surface after synthesis gas treatment was as follows: ThNi$_5$ > UNi$_5$ > ZrNi$_5$ > Ni/ThO$_2$. Therefore, when the larger amounts of nickel segregated to the surface of the intermetallic, greater methanation activity was observed (Table 5). These results were consistent with some previous work done by Moldovan et al.,[94] who employed AES to study the same systems. The AES experiments, however, could not easily distinguish chemical states, whereas ESCA was able to determine that the Ni remained metallic during the reactions and the rare-earth component was oxidized.

Continuation of this study involved reoxidation of the extreme cases (ThNi$_5$ and ZrNi$_5$) to investigate the Ni–rare earth interaction. The experiment was performed by treating the intermetallic with H$_2$ and synthesis gas, then exposing the sample to a controlled amount of O$_2$. The samples were analyzed by ESCA to evaluate the degree of oxidation. The nickel on the ThNi$_5$ displayed a significantly greater degree of oxidation than that on the ZrNi$_5$ (Figure 21). This result indicates that the interaction between the Ni and Zr in ZrNi$_5$ is greater

**TABLE 6. ESCA Intensity Ratios of the Catalysts
Studied After Various Treatments**

	Treatment[a]	Ni $2p_{3/2}$/Th $4f_{7/2}$[c]	Percentage increase in Ni/M
ThNi$_5$	Fresh	0.46	—
	Reduced 2 hr	1.39	202
	Reacted 6 hr	3.00	525
	Treatment	Ni $2p_{3/2}$/U $4f_{7/2}$	Percentage increase in Ni/M
UNi$_5$	Fresh	0.48	—
	Reduced 2 hr	0.79	67
	Reacted 6 hr	1.06	121
	Treatment	Ni $2p_{3/2}$/Zr $3d_{5/2,3/2}$	Percentage increase in Ni/M
ZrNi$_5$	Fresh	1.05	—
	Reduced 2 hr	1.19	13
	Reduced 11 hr	2.22	111
	Reacted 6 hr[b]	2.29	118
	Reduced 2 hr at 350°C	1.49	42
	Reacted 24 hr at 350°C	3.42	242
	Treatment	Ni $2p_{3/2}$/Th $4f_{7/2}$	Percentage increase in Ni/M
Ni/ThO$_2$	Fresh	0.06	—
	Reduced 2 hr	0.06	0
	Reacted 6 hr	0.05	(−16)

[a] All reductions and reactions were performed at 300°C unless otherwise noted. Reaction gas mixture was CO + H$_2$ (1:3).
[b] Reaction following 11-hr reduction.
[c] Intensity ratios were measured with an uncertainty of ±5% rsd.

than the interaction between Ni and Th because of the smaller amount of oxidation which was observed. Also, the lesser degree of Ni surface segregation that occurred during H$_2$ and synthesis gas treatment for ZrNi$_5$ suggests greater interaction between the Ni and Zr. This greater interaction, which limits the amount of surface Ni, indicates why there is a variation in methanation activities among the rare-earth intermetallics. The degree of segregation, however, is

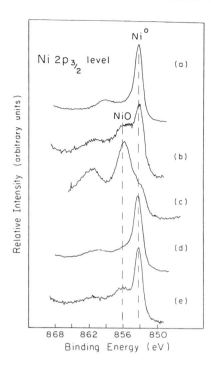

Figure 21. ESCA spectra of the Ni $2p_{3/2}$ core level of MNi$_5$ catalysts after reoxidation in air. (a) ThNi$_5$ after 6 hr CO/H$_2$ reaction; (b) exposure of a to air for 1 minute; (c) exposure of b to air for 2 weeks; (d) ZrNi$_5$ after 24 hrs CO/H$_2$ reaction; (e) exposure of d to air for 2 weeks. (After China et al.[93])

also a competitive process between the interaction of Ni and hydrogen[95] and the interaction between Ni and the rare-earth component. The intermetallics also indicated interaction with Co during methanation because the combined effect of CO and H$_2$ result in decomposition of the intermetallic, which produces a much larger surface area catalyst.

These brief and simple experiments analyzing rare-earth intermetallic catalysts before and after treatment by ESCA have displayed its capability of characterizing the surface and following surface changes as a function of treatment. In this manner a reasonable explanation for the variations in catalytic activity was obtained.

Raney Nickel Catalysts

Raney nickel catalysts have become very important in organic synthesis because they display some of the highest hydrogenation activities of any nickel catalysts. Raney nickel catalysts exhibit such efficient activity for hydrogenation that they have been employed in some analytical organic compound determinations.[96] Therefore, a good deal of research has been focused on the understanding of Raney nickel catalysts superior hydrogenation activity.

Recently, a few workers have employed surface analysis to characterize Raney nickel alloys and the activated catalyst.

Raney catalysts are prepared by leaching a Ni/Al alloy (usually 40:60 wt% Ni:Al) powder with concentrated base to remove the Al and produce a high-surface-area nickel catalyst. The alloys which are usually used are aluminum rich because the nickel-rich alloys resist leaching.[97] Leaching reactions can be carried out at various base concentrations, times, and leaching temperatures. These factors have been shown to alter the activity of this catalyst.[98]

The initial ESCA work on Raney catalysts was geared to the surface characterization of the Ni/Al alloys. The surface of the Ni/Al alloys resembles the surface of rare earth–nickel intermetallic compounds discussed previously. The major component on the surface is Al_2O_3 with small amounts of Al^0 and Ni^0.[99-101] These observations are consistent with a higher heat of formation for Al_2O_3 than for the nickel oxides.[102] Also, Al has a higher surface free energy, which energetically permits its segregation to the surface.[103]

Variation in surface segregation and surface reactivity as a function of bulk Ni/Al concentration was observed by using ESCA, AES, and SIMS.[101] Analysis of the Ni/Al intermetallic surface after polishing indicated that, as the bulk concentration of Al increased, the degree of Al surface segregation and the extent of Al oxidation increased. This was concluded by comparing the surface concentrations to the bulk concentrations of the alloys and by measuring the relative amount of Al^{3+} on the surface using ESCA. Also, it was determined that the degree of nickel enrichment on the surface after leaching was dramatically larger for the Al-rich alloys (Figure 22). Therefore, the leaching process was more effective in the Al-rich alloys, which is consistent with the polished alloys ESCA results[102] and previous classical surface determinations.[99] Work

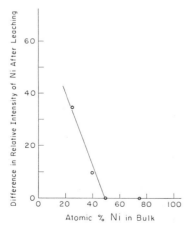

Figure 22. NaOH leaching results of Ni/Al alloys. The difference between the relative Ni 3p ESCA intensity of the leached and freshly polished alloys

$$\frac{I_{Ni\ 3p}}{I_{Ni\ 2p} + I_{Al\ 2p}}\ \text{leached} - \frac{I_{Ni\ 3p}}{I_{Ni\ 2p} + I_{Al\ 2p}}\ \text{polished}$$

is plotted versus the alloy bulk composition. (After Klein and Hercules.[104]

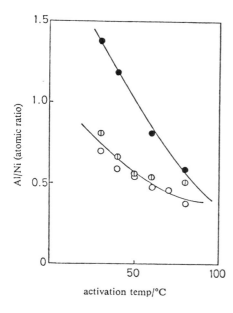

Figure 23. Atomic ratio of Al/Ni determined by ESCA versus the activation temperature for Raney nickel catalysts. ● 27 wt% Ni alloy, ○ 42 wt% Ni alloy, ○ 48 wt% Ni alloy. (After Okamoto et al.[100])

performed by Storp and colleagues on a mixed-phase Ni/Al alloy also indicated enhanced segregation for the Al-rich alloys.[99]

ESCA analysis was used to determine the effects of leaching temperature on the surface of the catalysts.[100] Okamoto et al.[100] determined that, using ESCA, the amount of surface Al decreased as the leaching temperature increased (Figure 23). These results were also confirmed by a similar study using AES.[104] Therefore, the higher leaching temperature facilitates removal of the leaching products and exposes more nickel. This result is consistent with higher catalyst activity for higher activation temperatures. Also, Okamoto et al.[100] have observed that the surface area increases as the surface Ni/Al atomic ratio increases.

Unfortunately, a problem exists when analyzing Raney nickel–activated catalysts by ESCA or AES.[104] After a short time (ca. 10 min) of leaching at a constant temperature the surface characteristics of the catalysts become constant (both concentration and chemical state). However, the leaching reaction continues to proceed. This was concluded because hydrogen was still being evolved beyond 10 min of leaching. Therefore, the activation reaction takes place at a greater depth than the sampling depths of the surface techniques, and so analysis of the total catalysts surface is not possible. The limited sampling depth of ESCA and AES can be responsible for contradictions between classical catalytic analysis and surface spectroscopy. For example, under the same activation conditions using the same alloys, classical adsorption determined that the amount of nickel on the surface[105] was about 30% greater than the amount of surface nickel determined by ESCA.[100] Therefore, under these conditions ESCA and AES do not have the ability to analyze the total surface of the Raney catalyst.

4. CONCLUDING REMARKS

The authors hope that this brief review has given the reader some insight into how ESCA has been applied to heterogeneous catalysis. ESCA has been clearly shown to be a valuable tool for analyzing these catalytic materials. However, one should keep in mind that this technique, as in all analytical techniques has its problems and limitations. Therefore, a newcomer in this field should attempt extensive literature and experimental research before tackling the problems of real-world catalysts.

ACKNOWLEDGMENTS

The authors would like to indicate that the work performed in our laboratories was funded as follows:

1. The nickel catalysts work was supported by the National Science Foundation under Grants CHE76-19452 and CHE78-00876.
2. The cobalt catalysts work was supported by the National Science Foundation under Grants CHE-7611255 and CHE-7918084.
3. The molybdenum catalysts work was supported by the National Science Foundation under Grant CHE78-00876 and by the United States Department of Energy under Grant DE-AC02-79#-R10 485.A00.
4. The nickel intermetallic work was supported by the National Science Foundation under Grant CHE78-00876.
5. The Raney catalysts work was supported by the National Science Foundation under Grant CHE78-00876.

REFERENCES

1. K. Siegbahn, C. Nordling, and E. Sokolowski, *Proceedings of the Rohovoth Conference on Nuclear Structure, 1957,* H. J. Lipkin, Ed., North-Holland Publs., Amsterdam, 1958, p. 291.
2. E. Sokolowski, C. Nordling, and K. Siegbahn, *Phys. Rev.,* **110**, 766 (1958).

3. D. R. Penn, *J. Electron Spectr.,* **9,** 29–40 (1976).

4. S. C. Fung, *J. Catalysis,* **58,** 454 (1979).

5. J. S. Brinen, J. L. Schmitt, W. R. Doughman, P. J. Achorn, L. A. Siegel, and W. N. Delgass, *J. Catalysis,* **40,** 295 (1975).

6. R. L. Chin, Ph.D. Thesis, University of Pittsburgh, 1980, p. 84.

7. C. N. Satterfield, *Heterogeneous Catalysis in Practice,* McGraw-Hill, New York, 1980.

8. J. J. Burton and R. L. Garten, Eds., *Advanced Materials in Catalysis,* Academic Press, New York, 1977.

9. B. C. Gates, J. R. Katzer, and G. C. A. Schuit, *Chemistry of Catalytic Processes,* McGraw-Hill, New York, 1979.

10. N. W. Delgass, G. L. Haller, R. Kellerman, and J. H. Lunsford, *Spectroscopy in Heterogeneous Catalysis,* Academic Press, New York, 1979.

11. K. Larson, E. Sokolowski, K. Siegbahn, and E. Stenhage, *Acta Chem. Scand.,* **20,** 2880 (1966).

12. J. C. Riviere, *Contemp. Phys.,* **14,** 513 (1973).

13. W. M. Riggs and M. J. Parker, in *Methods of Surface Analysis,* A. W. Czanderna, Ed., Elsevier, New York, 1975, Chap. 4.

14. D. A. Shirley, in *Topics in Applied Physics,* Vol. 26, M. Cardona and L. Ley, Eds., Springer, New York, 1978, Chap. 4.

15. G. K. Wertheim and P. H. Citrin, in *Topics in Applied Physics,* Vol. 26, M. Cardona and L. Ley, Eds., Springer, New York, 1978, Chap. 5.

16. J. S. Brien, *Acc. Chem. Res.,* **9,** 86 (1976).

17. W. E. Shwartz and D. M. Hercules, *Anal. Chem.,* **43,** 1774 (1971).

18. C. D. Wagner, *Anal. Chem.,* **44,** 1050–1053 (1972).

19. F. P. J. M. Kerkhof and J. A. Moulijn, *J. Phys. Chem.,* **83,** 1612 (1979).

20. D. Briggs, Ed., *Handbook of X-ray and Ultraviolet Photoelectron Spectroscopy,* Heyden, London, 1977.

21. G. K. Wertheim, *J. Electron Spectr.,* **6,** 239–251 (1975).

22. D. M. Hercules, *ESCA and Auger Spectroscopy,* ACS Audio Course, American Chemical Society, Washington, D.C., 1979.

23. W. F. Maddams, *Appl. Spectr.,* **34,** 245–267 (1980).

24. A. F. Carley and R. W. Joyner, *J. Electron Spectr.,* **16,** 1–23, (1979).

25. G. Johansson, J. Hedman, A. Berndtsson, M. Klasson, and R. Nilsson, *J. Electron Spectr.,* **2,** 295–317 (1973).

26. K. S. Kim, N. Winograd, and R. E. Davis, *J. Amer. Chem. Soc.,* **93,** 6296 (1971).

27. W. Bremser and F. Linneman, *Chem. Ztg.,* **95,** 1011 (1971).

28. D. Bitteridge, J. C. Carver, and D. M. Hercules, *J. Electron Spectr.,* **2,** 327–334 (1975).

29. T. A. Patterson, J. C. Carver, D. E. Leydon, and D. M. Hercules, *J. Phys. Chem.*, **80**, 1700–1708 (1976).

30. R. W. Joyner and M. W. Roberts, *J. Chem. Soc. Faraday Trans. I*, **70**, 1819 (1974).

31. D. C. Frost, A. Ishitani, and C. A. MacDowell, *Mol. Phys.*, **24**, 861 (1972).

32. C. A. Tolman, W. M. Riggs, W. J. Linn, C. M. King, and R. C. Wendt, *Inorg. Chem.*, **12**, 2770 (1973).

33. J. S. Brinen, *Acc. Chem. Res.*, **9**, 86 (1976).

34. D. S. Zingg, L. E. Makovsky, R. E. Tischer, F. R. Brown, and D. M. Hercules, *J. Phys. Chem.*, **84**, 2989–2906 (1980).

35. R. B. Moyers and M. W. Roberts, *J. Catalysis*, **49**, 216–224 (1977).

36. S. Evans, *J. Chem. Soc. Faraday Trans.*, **71**, 1044 (1975).

37. C. D. Wagner, L. H. Gale, and R. H. Raymond, *Anal. Chem.*, **51**, 466–482 (1979).

38. C. D. Wagner, in *Handbook of X-ray and Ultraviolet Photoelectron Spectroscopy*, D. Briggs, Ed., Heyden, London, 1977, pp. 387–392.

39. I. Nakai, Y. Sugitani, K. and Nagashima, Y. Niwa, *J. Inorg. Nucl. Chem.*, **40**, 789–791 (1978).

40. J. Grimblot, J. P. Bonnelle, and J. P. Beaufils, *J. Electron Spectro.*, **8**, 437–447 (1976).

41. V. I. Nefedov, Y. N. Salyn, G. Leonhardt, and R. Scheife, *J. Electron Spectro.*, **10**, 121 (1977).

42. T. E. Madey, C. D. Wager, and A. Joshi, *J. electron Spectr.*, **10**, 359 (1977).

43. V. I. Nefedov, Y. N. Salyn, A. A. Chertkov, and L. N. Padurets, *Zh. Neorg. Khim.*, **22**, 1715 (1977).

44. I. Ikemoto, K. Ishii, S. Kinoshito, H. Kuroda, M. A. A. Franco, and J. M. Thomas, *J. Solid State Chem.*, **17**, 425 (1976).

45. V. I. Nefedor, D. Gati, B. F. Dzhurinskii, N. P. Sergushin, and Y. N. Salyn, *Zh. Neorg. Khim*, **20**, 2307 (1975).

46. M. Wu and D. M. Hercules, *J. Phys. Chem.*, **83**, 2003 (1979).

47. J. C. Vedrine, C. Hollinger, and M. T. Duc, *J. Phys. Chem.*, **82**, 1515 (1978).

48. J. Shyu and D. M. Hercules, to be submitted.

49. M. Houalla and B. Delmon, *J. Phys. Chem.*, **84**, 2194–2199 (1980).

50. R. B. Shalvoy, P. J. Reucroft, and B. H. Davis, *J. Catalysis*, **56**, 336–348 (1979).

51. R. B. Shalvoy, P. J. Reucroft, and B. H. Davis, *J. Vacuum Sci. Technol.*, **17**, 209–210 (1980).

52. D. W. Goodman, R. D. Kelley, T. E. Madey, and J. T. Yates, Jr., in *Hydrocarbon Synthesis from Carbon Monoxide and Hydrogen*, E. L. Kugler and

F. W. Steffgen, Eds., American Chemical Society, Washington, D.C., 1978, Chap. 1.

53. J. Grimblot, A. D'Huysser, J. P. Bonnelle, and J. P. Beaufils, *J. Electron Spectr.*, **6**, 71–76 (1975).

54. J. P. Bonnelle, J. Grimblot, and A. D'Huysser, *J. Electron Spectr.*, **7**, 151–162 (1975).

55. J. Grimblot and J. P. Bonnelle, *J. Electron Spectr.*, **9**, 449–457 (1976).

56. R. L. Chin and D. M. Hercules, *J. Phys. Chem.*, **86**, 360 (1982).

57. R. B. Greegor, F. A. Lytle, R. L. Chin, and D. M. Hercules, *J. Phys. Chem.*, **85**, 1232 (1981).

58. A. Cimino and B. A. DeAngelis, *J. Catalysis,* **36**, 11 (1975).

59. A. W. Miller, W. Atkinson, M. Barber, and P. Swift, *J. Catalysis,* **22**, 140 (1971).

60. A. W. Armour, P. C. H. Mitchell, B. Tolkesson, and R. Larsson, *J. Less Common Metals,* **36**, 361 (1974).

61. P. Gajardo, R. I. Declerak-Grimee, G. Delvaux, P. Olodo, J. M. Zabala, P. Canesson, P. Grange, and B. Delmon, *J. Less Common Metals,* **54**, 311 (1977).

62. P. Ratnasamy, *J. Catalysis,* **40**, 137 (1975).

63. F. A. Cotton and G. Wilkinson, *Advanced Inorganic Chemistry,* 3rd ed., Wiley, New York, 1971.

64. E. L. Aptekar, M. G. Chadinov, A. M. Alekseev, and O. V. Krylov, *React. Kinet. Catalysis Lett.,* **1**, 493 (1974).

65. J. Masson, B. Delmon, and J. Nechtschein, *C. R. Acad. Sci., Paris, Ser. C,* **266**, 1257 (1968).

66. M. DuFaux, M. Che, and C. Naccache, *J. Chim. Phys.* **67**, 527 (1970).

67. F. E. Massoth, *J. Catalysis,* **30**, 204 (1973).

68. S. Abdo, M. Lo Jacono, R. B. Clarkson, and W. K. Hall., *J. Catalysis,* **36**, 330 (1975).

69. W. K. Hall and F. E. Massoth, *J. Catalysis,* **34**, 41 (1974).

70. N. Giordano, J. C. J. Bart, A. Vaghi, A. Castellon, and G. Martinotti, *J. Catalysis,* **36**, 81 (1975).

71. F. R. Brown, L. E. Makovsky, and K. H. Rhee, *J. Catalysis,* **50**, 385 (1977).

72. Y. Okamoto, H. Tomioka, Y. Katoh, T. Imanaka, and S. Teranishi, *J. Phys. Chem.,* **84**, 1833 (1980).

73. K. S. Chung and F. E. Massoth, *J. Catalysis,* **64**, 320 (1980).

74. F. R. Brown and L. E. Makovski, submitted for publication.

75. A. Cimino and B. A. DeAngelis, *J. Catalysis,* **36**, 11 (1975).

76. Y. Okamoto, T. Imanaka, and S. Teranishi, *J. Catalysis,* **65**, 448 (1980).

77. Y. Okamoto, H. Nakano, T. Shimokawa, T. Imanaha, and S. Teranishi, *J. Catalysis,* **50**, 447 (1977).

78. F. E. Massoth, *J. Catalysis,* **54**, 450–451 (1978).

79. J. S. Brinen and W. D. Armstrong, J. Catalysis, **54**, 57 (1978).

80. J. B. McKinley, in *Catalysis,* Vol. 5, P. Emmet, Ed., Reinhold, New York, 1957, p. 405.

81. V. H. S. DeBeer, C. Bevelander, T. H. M. Van Sint Tiet, P. G. A. J. Werter, and C. H. Amberg, *J. Catalysis,* **43**, 68 (1976).

82. Y. Okamoto, T. Shimokawa, T. Imanaka, and S. Teranishi, *J. Catalysis,* **57**, 153 (1979).

83. K. T. Ng and D. M. Hercules, *J. Phys. Chem.,* **80**, 2094 (1976).

84. R. M. Triedman, J. J. Freeman, and F. W. Lytle, *J. Catalysis,* **55**, 10 (1978).

85. E. S. Shpiro, V. I.Avaev, G. V. Antoshin, M. A. Ryashentseva, and K. H. M. Minachev, *J. Catalysis,* **55**, 402 (1978).

86. G. Mattogno, G. Polsonetti, and G. R. Tauszik, *J. Electron Spectr.,* **14**, 237 (1978).

87. V. T. Coon, T. Takeshita, W. E. Wallace, and R. S. Craig, *J. Phys. Chem.,* **80**, 1878 (1976).

88. A. Elattar, T. Takeshita, W. E. Wallace, and R. S. Craig, *Science,* **196**, 1093 (1977).

89. C. A. Luengo, A. L. Cabrera, H. B. McKay, and M. B. Maple, *J. Catalysis,* **47**, 1 (1977).

90. G. B. Atkinson and L. J. Nicks, *J. Catalysis,* **46**, 417 (1977).

91. T. Takeshita, W. E. Wallace, and R. S. Craig, *Inorg. Chem.,* **13**, 2282 (1978).

92. H. C. Siegmann, L. Schlapbach, and C. R. Brundle, *Phys. Rev. Lett.,* **40**, 972 (1978).

93. R. L. Chin, A. Elattar, W. E. Wallace, and D. M. Hercules, *J. Phys. Chem.,* **84**, 2985 (1980).

94. A. G. Moldovan, A. Elattar, W. E. Wallace, and R. S. Craig, *J. Solid State Chem.,* **25**, 23 (1978).

95. K. Soga, H. Imamura, and S. Ikeda, *Nippon Kagaku Kaishi,* **9**, 1304 (1977).

96. H. Siggia, *Quantitative Organic Analysis via Functional Groups,* 4th ed., Wiley, 1979.

97. J. Freel, W. J. M. Pieters, and R. B. Anderson, *J. Catalysis,* **16**, 281–291 (1970).

98. J. Freel, S. D. Robertson, and R. B. Anderson, *J. Catalysis,* **18**, 243–248 (1970).

99. S. Storp, K. Berresheim, and M. Wilmers, *Surface Interface Anal.,* **1**, 96 (1979).

100. Y. Okamoto, Y. Nitta, T. Imanaka, and S. Teranish, *J. Chem. Soc. Faraday Trans. I,* **76**, 998 (1980).

101. J. C. Klein and D. M. Hercules, *Annal. Chem.,* **53**, 754 (1981).

102. A. R. Miedema, *Z. Metallk.,* **69**, 455 (1978).

103. P. Bouwman, L. H. Joneman, and A. A. Holscher, *Surface Sci.,* **35**, 8–33 (1973).

104. J. C. Klein and D. M. Hercules, unpublished work.

105. S. D. Robertson and R. B. Anderson, *J. Catalysis,* **41**, 405–411 (1976).

CHAPTER

9

USE OF ESCA IN
THE CHARACTERIZATION OF
HETEROGENEOUS MATERIALS

H. WINDAWI*

Corporate Research Center
UOP Inc.
Des Plaines, Illinois

and

C. D. WAGNER

Surfex Company
Oakland, California

1. INTRODUCTION

Instruments for the ESCA technique detect electrons emerging from an area of a solid of the order of 1-100 mm^2 and from depths to ca. 100 Å. Materials that are heterogeneous on this scale pose special problems. Application of the useful quantitative surface-analysis procedure provides data that depend not only upon

---

*Work was carried out while the author was affiliated with the Center for Catalytic Science and Technology, University of Delaware, Newark, Delaware.

the usual factors involved with homogeneous systems but also the relative areas occupied on the surface by the different phases. Procedures for identification of chemical states requiring charge referencing are subject to ambiguities introduced by differential charging. On the other hand, differential charging of the phases offers the opportunity to identify the components of each phase. This chapter treats the special problems in applying ESCA to multiphase materials.

2. QUANTITATIVE ANALYSIS

The usual quantitative analysis procedure used in ESCA involves measurement of the peak areas of the elemental strong lines and division of those areas by suitable sensitivity factors. This provides data on the relative number of atoms of each element present. The assumption must be made that the material is homogeneous, in order to apply the sensitivity factors. Application to a heterogeneous system then provides only data on the relative number of atoms *detected*. Translation of that tabulation into something meaningful to the analyst requires more information. For example, catalysts with alumina, silica, or zirconia supports are not homogeneous. The size of the high-surface-area silica particle is of the order of 40 Å, and those of alumina and zirconia are larger. The catalytic element resides on the surface of these particles, either as atomic or agglomerated species, or both. The catalyst in dimensions meaningful in ESCA is homogeneous neither in depth nor in lateral direction. This poses special problems in drawing conclusions about catalyst structure from relative ESCA line intensities.

For supported catalyst the mean free paths of the electrons generated by the ESCA instrument are almost always smaller (5-50 Å[1]) than the particle diameter of the support material. One can then assume a model whereby any detected electron originating from the supported catalytic element (denoted henceforth as *element*) cannot have passed through the support. In other words, only element exposed in line of sight view to the analyzer will be detectable. For simplicity the model assumes the support is made up of spheres arranged in an overall plane normal to the analyzer direction, with element in much smaller cubical aggregates on the support surface having a uniform thickness of n atomic layers.

The specific surface area of the support is represented by A_s, in square centimeters per gram, the area of the sample from which electrons are detected by the spectrometer is denoted by A, the density of the element is d in grams per cubic centimeter, the number of atomic layers is n, the thickness of a layer is s, the electron mean free path in the element is λ, and the specific emission rate of electrons under the incident instrumental x-ray flux in the direction of the analyzer is J_0 in electrons per cubic centimeter per second.

The emission rate from the pure element may now be calculated. The emission rate emerging from the surface but originating from an infinitesimally thick layer n layers from the surface is given by

$$dI = AJ_0 e^{-ns/\lambda} dn \qquad (1)$$

and integrating between 0 and n,

$$I = AJ_0\lambda[1 - e^{-ns/\lambda}] \qquad (2)$$

When ns/λ is very small,

$$I = AJ_0 ns \qquad (3)$$

and when it is very large,

$$I_{e\infty} = AJ_0\lambda \qquad (4)$$

where $I_{e\infty}$ stands for intensity from bulk material. Then the range of values goes from monolayer to the bulk:

$$I_{(n=1)} = AJ_0 s \qquad (5)$$

$$I_{(n=\infty)} = AJ_0\lambda \qquad (6)$$

With platinum, for example, the range is about 10-fold, from $s = 2.5$ Å to $\lambda = $ ca. 25Å.

As indicated above, when the element is mounted on a support it does not ordinarily cover the surface but is present as small islands or aggregates. The weight of the element on the line of sight surface can be calculated in the following way. The line-of-sight surface may be approximated by spheres of support with a micro roughness factor of 2, that is, the surface area of the spheres as measured by nitrogen adsorption is twice that calculated from the diameter. If the surface of the sample is assumed to be composed of spheres in closest packing, the actual surface area exposed to the view of the analyzer is then 3.6 times the overall dimensional area A of the sample. This is then essentially a double-roughness factor, and let us term it r in the equations below and evaluate it at 4.0.

We assume that the metal rests randomly on the macrosurface of the support particle. The weight of the element on the line of sight surface, for sufficiently low loadings, is

$$W_e = \frac{LAr}{100 \, A_s} \tag{7}$$

where L is the loading in wt% of the element. This leads to the area of the element from which electrons are detected:

$$A_e = \frac{LAr}{100 \, A_s \, dns} \tag{8}$$

The electron emission rate is affected as in Equation 2 by interactions of the electrons passing through the element on the way to the analyzer. The integrated number per second emerging from n layers is, adapting Equation 2,

$$I_e = A_e J_0 \lambda \, (1 - e^{-ns/\lambda}) \tag{9}$$

For the special case of the element on a support, the electron emission rate is a function of the area of the sample, the fractional area covered by the element, the thickness of the metal aggregates, the electron mean free path, and the specific volume emission rate. Combining Equations 8 and 9,

$$I_e = \frac{A J_0 rL}{100 \, A_s d} \left[\frac{\lambda(1 - e^{-ns/\lambda})}{ns} \right] \tag{10}$$

From Equation 4

$$\frac{I_e}{I_{e\infty}} = \frac{rL}{100 \, A_s d} \left[\frac{1 - e^{-ns/\lambda}}{ns} \right] \tag{11}$$

where $I_{e\infty}$ is the intensity from bulk metal. When I_e comes from a very thin layer, where ns is small relative to λ, we have the limit

$$\frac{I_e}{I_{e\infty}} = \frac{rL}{100 \, A_s d} \left(\frac{1}{\lambda} \right) \tag{12}$$

Where *ns* is comparable to λ, Equation 11 applies; and where *ns* is large compared to λ,

$$\frac{I_e}{I_{e_\infty}} = \frac{rL}{100\,A_s d}\left(\frac{1}{ns}\right)$$

(13)

so that then the intensity is inversely proportional to the particle thickness. The multiplying factor represents the thickness of the metal on the model catalyst surface if it completely covered it uniformly.

As illustrations we apply these equations to some systems, as shown in Figure 1.

Silver on Alumina

This is suggested as an example of a high-loading, low-surface-area catalyst. One can imagine materials used ranging from 5–15% silver and surface areas for the alumina support in the range 0.1–1.0 m^2/g. The combination of loading and surface area requires that uniform coverage of alumina be of the order of 100 atoms thick, so that Equation 13 applies. Sintering to one particle per square centimeter of surface would lead to a particle thickness of ca 10^6 atoms, or 200

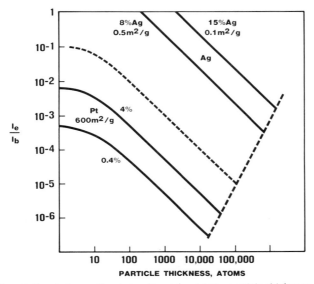

Figure 1. The relation between line intensity and catalytic particle thickness: I_e/I_{e_∞} is the ratio between the photoelectron line intensity from the catalytic element and the same element in bulk form.

μm. The normal range of catalyst would probably have the silver in the micrometer range, somewhat above the level corresponding to complete coverage. As shown in Figure 1, sintering should reduce the Ag $3d_{5/2}$ line intensity inversely as particle size grows.

Platinum on Silica Gel

This represents the opposite extreme of a low-loading, high-surface-area catalyst. Here the high surface area (600 m^2/g) would require theoretically a loading of 75 g/100 g catalyst to form monolayer coverage. At only 4.0% or 0.4%, as shown in Figure 1, atomic dispersion is of course feasible. The limiting highest value for I_e/I_{e_∞} is given by Equation 12. Between $n = 1$ and $n = 20$, Equation 11 applies; above $n = 20$, the particles are large enough that Equation 13 takes over.

The foregoing analysis shows that for supported materials of particle size greater than 50 Å the ESCA line intensity at constant loading should be inversely proportional to the linear dimension (thickness). For particle size less than 50 Å the intensity approaches a constant value, independent of particle size as it approaches atomic dimensions.

Studies reported often are in terms of intensity of a line from the element versus intensity of a line from the support (I_s). The fraction of the area covered by the element is derived from Equation 8:

$$\frac{A_e}{Ar} = \frac{L}{100\, A_s dns} = f \tag{14}$$

and the intensity of signal from the support I_s in the catalyst relative to that from support alone, I_{s_0}, is

$$\frac{I_s}{I_{s_0}} = 1 - f + fe^{-ns/\lambda_s} \tag{15}$$

where the first and second terms represent signal from uncovered support, and the third term includes signal penetrating a sufficiently thin deposit of the element; λ_s is the mean free path of the photoelectron from the support as it passes through the element. The ratio I_e/I_s then is given by

$$\frac{I_e}{I_s} = \frac{I_{e_\infty}(1 - e^{-ns/\lambda})f}{I_{s_0}[1 - f(1 - e^{-ns/\lambda_s})]} \tag{16}$$

and this is identical with the equation developed by Angevine and associates for a similar model.[2]

If f is a small fraction, or if ns is small relative to λ_s, then

$$\frac{I_e}{I_s} = \frac{I_{e\infty}(1 - e^{-ns/\lambda})L}{I_{s_0} \, ns \, 100 \, A_s d} \tag{17}$$

and the function is similar in form to Equation 11 for $I_e/I_{e\infty}$. Then, if ns is small relative to λ and λ_s

$$\frac{I_e}{I_s} = \frac{I_{e\infty}L}{I_{s_0} \, 100 \, A_s d\lambda} \tag{18}$$

and if ns is large while f is small,

$$\frac{I_e}{I_s} = \frac{I_{e\infty}L}{I_{s_0} \, 100 \, A_s dns} \tag{19}$$

Many catalytic systems seem to fall into these categories with low metal loadings and high-surface-area support, or both. With such systems, for a constant particle size of the catalytic element the intensity ratio of lines from supported and support materials should be proportional to the loading of the supported element. Brinen[3] shows such a plot (Figure 2) of a relationship for MoO_3 supported on Al_2O_3. The Mo $3d_{5/2}$ line intensity divided by the Al $2p$ intensity increased linearly from 1–12% MoO_3.

Another important observation is the effect of heat treatment on intensity of ESCA lines. For example, sintering of supported particles to form particles of larger size will lead to a decrease in intensity of supported element relative to that of the support. Brinen et al.[4] report data on a rhodium on charcoal catalyst prepared by reduction under different conditions. The intensity ratio Rh $3d$/C $1s$ decreased as the particles of rhodium increased in size from 20 to 250 Å. However, the change was not linear for the larger particles, as Equation 19 predicts. This may be because the 850 m^2/g carbon used has a particle size smaller than the mean free path, but this deviates from the assumptions of the model used on deriving Equation 19.

Angevine et al.[2] utilized a set of Pt/SiO_2 catalysts, including a set examined by Scharpen[5] plus another set of similar materials, including, in all, 12 catalysts ranging from 0.38% to 3.7% Pt, with silica supports 245–526 m^2/g in surface area. Dispersions ranged from 7–100% (percentage of Pt atoms on the surface of the Pt particles), meaning the average particle diameter ranged from 85 atoms down to single atoms. Four of the catalysts were made by impregnation; the other eight were made by ion exchange. Angevine and colleagues showed that nine of the catalysts fit close to a straight line on a plot of $I(Pt\ 4f)/I(Si\ 2p)$

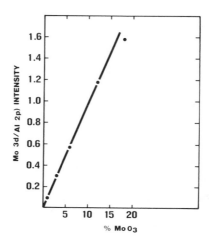

Figure 2. Intensity ratios for molybdenum oxide/alumina catalysts, plotted as a function of molybdenum oxide loading. (From Brinen.[3] Copyright ASTM, reprinted with permission.)

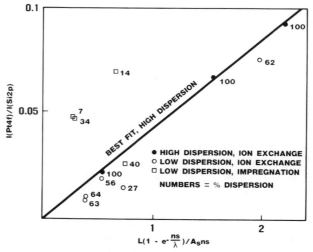

Figure 3. Intensity ratios for platinum/silica catalysts, plotted against $L(1 - e^{-ns/\lambda})/nsA_s$. (Data from Angevine et al.[2])

198

versus L/nsA_s, in accordance with Equation 19. They were stretching the applicability of that equation, since four of the catalysts were intermediate in dispersion ($ns \approx \lambda$) and three required Equation 18. Use of the more general Equation 17 with their data produces the slightly modified plot shown in Figure 3: $I(Pt)/I(Si)$ versus $L(1 - e^{-ns/\lambda})/nsA_s$. The four that conform the least are the lowest dispersion, three of which were prepared by impregnation. Angevine et al. attribute the deviation to the effect of the preparative method in producing nonideal distribution of particles in the high surface area structure.

At this point it is clear that the ratio I_e/I_s for these materials need bear no resemblance to that expected from a homogeneous mixture of platinum and silica. If we use empirically derived sensitivity factors for Pt $4f$/Si $2p$ of 4.6 and 0.26,[6] we obtain calculated values for their three high dispersion samples that agree with their experimental values within ±15%. Use of theoretical cross sections for these transitions[7] raised the average by 6%. The calculated value (using the empirical factors) for one low-dispersion sample (34%) was 88% of the experimental value. All the other calculated values for the eight other samples of 7–64% dispersion were too high, two- to fivefold. This qualitative observation is expected for the model when the elemental particle size becomes large.

3. DETECTION OF SURFACE CONTAMINATION

A valuable practical use of the technique is the detection of surface contamination on any solid sample. As shown in Equations 5 and 6, the detection of a monolayer is readily accomplished, with the intensity of signal from a monolayer relative to that from the bulk of the same material given by

$$\frac{I_{(n=1)}}{I_{(n=\infty)}} = \frac{s}{\lambda} \tag{22}$$

where s is the thickness of a monolayer and λ is the mean free path of the photoelectron in the solid. This ratio is expected to range from 4% to 20%, depending mostly on the kinetic energy of the photoelectron used. The sensitivity is sufficient to detect segregation of elements to the surfaces of particular minor phases included in the surface layers. The detectability cannot be accomplished by any form of microscopy or by analytical techniques other than surface techniques such as ESCA, Auger-electron spectroscopy (AES) secondary-ion mass spectroscopy (SIMS), or ion-scattering spectroscopy (ISS). The generality of the ESCA technique is aided by the fact that the relative sensitivities of the elements are similar, within a factor of about 40.

The fact that a peak originates from extreme surface can be verified by comparing intensities at normal and glancing angles. Detection of electrons emitted at glancing angles will enhance the relative contribution of electrons from surface atoms because the average path length through the surface layers is enhanced.

4. PROFILING BY DEPTH

Development of solid-state electrical devices has involved development of carefully defined systems heterogeneous in the vertical direction. A variety of depth-profiling techniques has been developed to characterize these materials, ordinarily involving erosion by energetic ions. This aspect was discussed in previous chapters of this volume. It should be pointed out that the characterization of the chemical states of elements at depths exposed by these techniques is very difficult because chemical bonds are broken and created in the exposed surface by the ion bombardment.

5. DETECTION OF COMPONENTS OF EACH PHASE

Irradiation of samples in the ESCA technique tends to develop a positive charge in the sample surface because of net electron emission. With insulators this can pose a problem in determining the electron energy (see below). The extent of charge is dependent[8] upon:

1. X-ray flux
2. Photoelectric cross section, summed over all possible transitions
3. Distribution in energy and number of electrons emitted from the atoms per photon absorbed
4. Mean free paths of the emitted and energy-degraded electrons
5. Flux and energy distribution of electrons impinging upon the sample from the vacuum space
6. Effective electron affinity of the sample surface.
7. Conductivity of the particle to the adjacent phase or to the sample holder

Factors 1 and 5 are properties of the spectrometer operation. Factor 5 involves electrons scattered from the window of the x-ray tube and from the internal spectrometer surfaces. All factors except 1 and 5 are properties of the sample, and with phases composed of large particles, if conductivity is sufficiently low, differential charging can occur. While this might seem to make analysis more complex, it can actually assist, because factor 5 can be artificially modified by adding electrons from an electron source or by biasing the sample relative to ground to change the potential gradients in the sample chamber. Changing factor 5 can change the extent of charge on different phases by different amounts.

Brinen[9] has illustrated the principle applied to insulating domains on an otherwise conducting sample. Addition of low-energy electrons from a "flood gun" causes lines in the spectrum originating from the insulating domains to move to higher kinetic energy. Those from the conducting phase do not change. However, one does not need a conducting phase to illustrate the effect. In Figure 4 is shown the carbon spectrum from a catalyst sample. Two carbon lines ca. 6 eV apart are evident. Addition of slow electrons in the spectrometer vacuum causes both lines to move to higher kinetic energy, but by different amounts, so that they were only about 4 eV apart. The higher-binding-energy line, moving the largest amount, moved in concert with all the other lines in the spectrum and comes from the adventitious hydrocarbon on the catalyst. The low-binding-energy line was interpreted to be from particles of carbon (graphite) added in the formulation of the catalyst. Graphite is known to charge relatively little under ESCA conditions,[8] compared to materials of higher cross section and large bandgap (presence of the latter leads to large mean free paths in the low-energy secondary electrons).

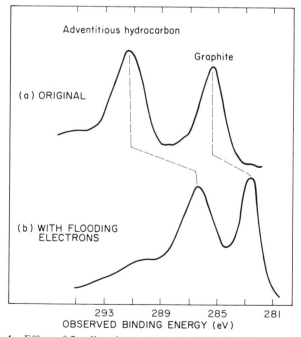

Figure 4.   Effect of flooding electrons on two carbon lines from a catalyst.

It should be realized that a noncontinuous second phase on an insulator will charge independently, whether it is a conductor or an insulator. It is possible to have a continuous conducting phase electrically connected to the spectrometer, an insulating support phase, and a noncontinuous phase of conducting particles mounted on the insulating support. In this case the support and noncontinuous conducting phase charge independently, while the continuous conducting phase is grounded and does not charge. Addition or subtraction of the electrons in the vacuum space decreases or increases the charge on the two charging phases independently.

6. IDENTIFICATION OF CHEMICAL STATE

Identification of chemical state in the separate phases of heterogeneous systems is a challenge. Ordinarily with homogeneous samples one uses the line energies and compares them with line energies (photoelectron binding energies and Auger kinetic energies) of standard chemical states. Doing this with insulators requires determining the extent of charge. This is done by observing the location of the C $1s$ line from adventitious surface hydrocarbon or the Au $4f_{7/2}$ line from an added partial coating of evaporated gold, comparing the results with C $1s$ at 284.6–285.0 eV or Au $4f_{7/2}$ at 83.8–84.0 eV. (There has not yet been consensus on the exact appropriate values for these materials in an uncharged sample.) One cannot use the electron flood gun, or "neutralizer," to remove the excess charge because samples can acquire a negative charge and there is no general method for stopping at neutrality. Lewis and Kelly[10] have shown that with sufficient flooding monoenergetic electrons the sample surface acquires the same potential relative to the vacuum level as the bombarding electrons. At that point, relative to the Fermi level, which is the usual reference level for all line energy data, the different phases are charged differentially to the extent of the difference in their work functions.

In a two-phase system one frequently encounters two C $1s$ lines, one associated with each phase. If one knows approximately the charging characteristics of each phase or if one knows the chemical state of one constituent in one phase, one can assign the carbon lines to the respective phases. With use of the flooding electrons, one can also determine the tracking of the carbon lines with the respective elements as the lines shift in energy. Charge referencing can thus be done on the independent phases. If this is not possible, another method is the use of an elemental constituent as a charge reference, for example, Al $2p$ in alumina, or an element that exhibits virtually no chemical shift in the photoelectron line, such as sodium or potassium.

There are spectral properties that are independent of static charge and therefore do not require a charge reference. In general, Auger lines have larger chemi-

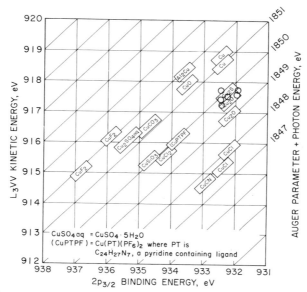

Figure 5. The two-dimensional chemical state plot for copper. Line positions from six unknown chemical states are superimposed.

cal shifts than photoelectron lines, because the doubly charged final state in the Auger transition acquires more screening energy from electrons of the surrounding polarizable medium. Therefore the difference in kinetic energy between the Auger electrons and photoelectrons of an element is a property that also has a chemical shift, and this property, the Auger parameter, can be useful. Data on this can be obtained in the normal ESCA configuration for the elements O, F, Na, Mg, Ti, V, Cr, Mn, Fe, Co, Ni, Cu, Zn, Ga, Ge, As, Se, Ru, Rh, Pd, Ag, Cd, In, Sn, Sb, Te, I, Xe, Cs, and Ba.[11] If charge referencing is feasible, two-dimensional chemical state plots are most useful. Shown in Figure 5 is such a plot for copper. Photoelectron energies are plotted on the abscissa, Auger energies on the ordinate, and the diagonal grid is that of the Auger parameter, the difference between the kinetic energy of the Auger line and that of the photoelectron line. One can equally well plot the binding energy of the photoelectron line in the reverse direction, as is done here. In that case, addition of the Auger kinetic energy and the photoelectron binding energy equals the Auger parameter plus the photon energy, which is the grid displayed in Figure 5. Note that the forms of cuprous copper exhibit essentially no chemical shift in the photoelectron line but significant chemical shifts in the Auger line. The six circles indicate values for six unknown samples containing Cu, O, S, and Cl. Clearly in these samples the copper was neither copper metal nor a copper chloride. The absence of shakeup lines indicated it to be cuprous and not cupric, confirming the conclusion from the photoelectron line energy itself. The unknown is probably Cu_2S, although there is some uncertainty in the Cu_2O line energy, as shown by the two values from different laboratories displayed.

Other elements also can be included in this technique under certain circumstances. The Auger *NOO* lines may be of use for Hg, Tl, Pb, and Bi, but thus far their feasibility has not been tested. They are of low kinetic energy: 80–100 eV. With easily applied special measures one can utilize the bremsstrahlung component of the x-rays[12] to generate Auger lines of Al, Si, P, S, and Cl, which are of high kinetic energy, appearing in an ESCA spectrum at higher kinetic energy than the Fermi level on the binding-energy scale.[13] Other elements not in the above groups can only be included by using added electron excitation or by using x-ray photons of higher energy, from anodes of elements such as titanium, silver, zirconium, or gold.[14] The Auger lines become of special importance when the chemical shifts in the photoelectron lines are minimal, as illustrated with cuprous copper, above. Other elements where this is the case are Na, K, Zn, Ag, Cd, In, Cs, and Ba.

Auger transitions with final states in valence levels yield Auger line distributions unique for each chemical state. These Auger electrons, usually of relatively low kinetic energy, can thus be useful for identification purposes. The *KVV* lines of C, N, and O, the *LVV* lines of Si, P, S, Cl, Ti, V, Cr, Mn, Fe, Co, and Ni, and the *MVV* lines of Y, Zr, Nb, Mo, Ru, and Rh all show promise in this respect. The varied patterns in the oxygen Auger group have been reported.[15] In Figure 6 an example is shown of different line shapes encountered with different forms of nickel on a catalyst surface.

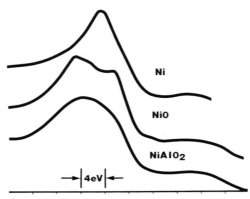

Figure 6. The *LVV* Auger group of nickel from different chemical states (as recorded for states supported on alumina).

Shakeup satellites are often observed with the photoelectron lines of paramagnetic ions. Both the separation from the parent line and the intensity are peculiar to each chemical state. Multiplet splitting in s and p lines is also observed. With s lines the splitting occurs to form two lines from one. With p lines, splitting occurs to form several lines, not resolved, and the effect is to increase the apparent p doublet separation. Both of these effects can be cataloged for different chemical states. In organic systems, a satellite of the C $1s$ line is evident with unsaturated or ring aromatic systems and distinguishes such a phase from saturated polymers.[16]

7. PROBLEMS WITH HIGHLY DISPERSED PHASES

Materials with one highly dispersed phase pose some very special problems. Atomically dispersed materials, of course, represent a special case in which the chemical state of the dispersed material has no resemblance to it in the bulk phase. Aggregates of dispersed material of linear dimensions of the order of 10 atoms or larger should have essentially bulk properties. The dimension of 10 atoms happens approximately to be about the length of the electron mean free path. Sizes intermediate between atomic and mean free path dimensions thus constitute a special case.

It is instructive to calculate the compositions at which this can be a problem. The ratio of weight of element to weight of support for a uniform monolayer is given by:

$$\frac{W_e}{W_s} = \frac{A_s M^{1/3} d^{2/3}}{(6 \times 10^{23})^{1/3}} = 1.2(10^{-4}) A_s M^{1/3} d^{2/3} \qquad (23)$$

where A_s is the specific area of the support in square meters per gram, M is the atomic weight of the supported element, and d is its density. The combined factors $M^{1/3} d^{2/3}$ can range from about 6 to 44, so the weight ratio ranges from 7 to $53 \times 10^{-8} A_s$. This ratio, corresponding to monolayer coverage, is also about the ratio that can give large amounts of independently spaced aggregates approximately 10 atoms thick. Figure 7 shows the relationship between loading and surface area that correspond to this density of supported atoms. Below this density one can also have aggregates this size, but more widely separated. Above this density one develops either larger particles, beyond the intermediate range, or a multilayer continuous phase. Thus, the curve represents the boundary above which this intermediate aggregation cannot take place.

For aggregate sizes in this intermediate range of about 10 atoms in diameter, half the atoms sampled are on the exterior of the particle and the signal is re-

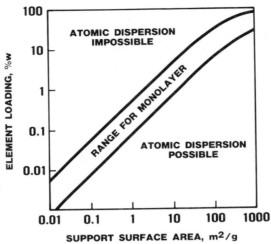

Figure 7. The relation between element loading and support surface area, for a monolayer.

ceived from atoms on the upper surface, the interior, and the lower interface with the support. It is not surprising, then, that for these intermediate dispersions lines are considerably broadened from environmental factors alone.

The environmental factors are of two kinds: the electron density on the atom, and electron screening from surrounding atoms of the ion left in the final state of the transition. Citrin et al.[17] have shown that there is a slight but measurable chemical shift from surface atoms of gold compared to the bulk. The effect will be considerably greater at a solid interface. For smaller aggregates, the point can be reached where electron screening of the positive final state is inhibited by the lack of a sufficient supply of conduction electrons. In this respect the shift in line energies between a free atom and the bulk state can be as much as 3 eV for photoelectron lines and 12 eV for Auger lines,[18] that is, enhancement in kinetic energy of the emitted electron occurs by screening with conduction electrons. With insulating aggregates, the polarizability as well as size also becomes a significant variable in this effect. Variations in particle size in this range can produce variable chemical shifts, variable Auger parameters, and broadened photoelectron and Auger lines.

Another question to consider with such intermediate-size particles is differential charging.[19] A sufficiently large particle will charge independently of the insulating support, whereas material atomically dispersed will assume the potential of the modified support phase. A mixture of intermediate-sized aggregates will produce mixed charging and broaden the lines. The dimensions required for differential charging are not well understood.

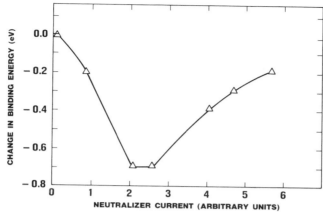

Figure 8. The effect of flooding electrons on the charge-referenced binding energy for Ni $2p_{3/2}$ in supported nickel oxide particles. (Adapted from reference 19.)

Some examples may serve to illustrate these principles. With a zirconia-supported ultradispersed rhodium oxide (D ~ 1), the Rh $3d_{5/2}$ line, the Zr $3d_{5/2}$ line, the O $1s$ line, and the C $1s$ line from adventitious hydrocarbon all shifted as flooding electrons were applied, to as much as 10 eV higher kinetic energy. The observed binding energy for the Rh $3d_{5/2}$ line, charge referenced to the C $1s$ line, remained constant at 307.75 ± 0.05 eV at five different electron flood settings. The value for bulk oxide powder was 308.4 eV. The atomically dispersed oxide charges with the support phase, and the binding energy is different from that of the bulk element, even though the valence state is similar.

In contrast, a nickel oxide on zirconia with particle size somewhat larger than 30 Å, as determined by x-ray diffraction, is affected differently from the adventitious hydrocarbon on the zirconia support. Binding energies for the Ni $2p_{3/2}$, C $1s$, O $1s$, and Zr $3d_{5/2}$ lines were recorded as the electron flooding was increased. The O $1s$ and Zr $3d_{5/2}$ lines moved with the C $1s$ line, to ±0.1 eV, as expected, but the Ni $2p_{3/2}$ line did not (as shown in Figure 8). The charge-referenced value decreased by 0.7 eV to a minimum of 854.2 eV and then increased. It seems reasonable to choose the minimum value as the best value, since it represents the minimum difference in charge between the phases, and since at that point the line width was at a minimum.[19]

The dimensions for independent particle charging are not yet known. Certainly 30 Å is an unexpectedly small dimension. The differential charge may well extend over a greater distance in the insulator support; 0.7 V in 30 Å is still 2,300,000 V/cm. It is clearly of considerable interest to explore further the dimensions required for differential charging, not only for dispersed supported phases, but also for thin films on substrates. The role of interfacial junctions is expected to be important in determining the spacially dependent charging properties.

REFERENCES

1. M. P. Seah and W. A. Dench, *Surface Interface Anal.,* **1**, 2 (1979).

2. P. J. Angevine, J. C. Vartuli, and W. N. Delgass, *Proc. Int. Congr. Catalysis,* **6**, 611 (1977).

3. J. S. Brinen, in *Applied Surface Analysis,* T. L. Barr and L. E. Davis, Eds., ASTM Monograph STP 699, American Society for Testing Materials, Philadelphia, 1978, p. 37.

4. J. S. Brinen, J. L. Schmitt, W. R. Doughman, P. J. Achorn, L. A. Siegel, and W. N. Delgass, *J. Catalysis,* **40**, 295 (1975).

5. L. H. Scharpen, *J. Electron Spectr.,* **5**, 369 (1974).

6. C. D. Wagner, L. E. Davis, M. V. Zeller, J. A. Taylor, R. H. Raymond, and L. H. Gale, *Surface Interface Anal.,* **3**, 211 (1981).

7. J. H. Scofield, *J. Electron Spectr.,* **8**, 129 (1976).

8. C. D. Wagner, *J. Electron Spectr.,* **18**, 345 (1980).

9. J. S. Brinen, *J. Electron Spectr.,* **5**, 377 (1974).

10. R. T. Lewis and M. A. Kelly, *J. Electron Spectr.,* **20**, 105 (1980).

11. C. D. Wagner, L. H. Gale, and R. H. Raymond, *Anal. Chem.,* **51**, 466 (1979).

12. J. E. Castle and R. H. West, *J. Electron Spectr.,* **18**, 355 (1980).

13. C. D. Wagner and J. A. Taylor, *J. Electron Spectr.,* **20**, 83 (1980).

14. C. D. Wagner, *J. Vacuum Sci. Technol.,* **15**, 518 (1978).

15. C. D. Wagner, D. A. Zatko, and R. H. Raymond, *Anal. Chem.,* **52**, 1445 (1980).

16. D. T. Clark, D. B. Adams, A. Dilks, J. Peeling, and H. R. Thomas, *J. Electron Spectr.,* **8**, 51 (1976).

17. P. H. Citrin, G. K. Wertheim, and Y. Baer, *Phys. Rev. Lett.,* **41**, 1425 (1978).

18. R. Kumpula, J. Vayrynen, T. Rantala, and S. Aksela, *J. Phys. C, Solid State Phys.,* **12**, L809 (1979).

19. H. Windawi, *J. Electron Spectr.,* **22**, 373 (1981).

INDEX

209